61 Cooperative Learning Activities in U.S. Histo

Kate O'Halloran

J. WESTON WALCH PUBLISHER

PORTLAND, MAINE

User's Guide
to
Walch Reproducible Books

As part of our general effort to provide educational materials which are as practical and economical as possible, we have designated this publication a "reproducible book." The designation means that purchase of the book includes purchase of the right to limited reproduction of all pages on which this symbol appears:

Here is the basic Walch policy: We grant to individual purchasers of this book the right to make sufficient copies of reproducible pages for use by all students of a single teacher. This permission is limited to a single teacher, and does not apply to entire schools or school systems, so institutions purchasing the book should pass the permission on to a single teacher. Copying of the book or its parts for resale is prohibited.

Any questions regarding this policy or requests to purchase further reproduction rights should be addressed to:

Permissions Editor
J. Weston Walch, Publisher
321 Valley Street • P. O. Box 658
Portland, Maine 04104-0658

1   2   3   4   5   6   7   8   9   10

ISBN 0-8251-2857-9

Contents

Teacher Guide and Reproducible Student Pages

To the Teacher

This book has been developed to let you offer your students the benefits of working in small groups while increasing their knowledge and understanding of U.S. history.

The 61 activities, arranged chronologically, cover the history of North America from the time before European contact through the present day. The variety of the activities will appeal to many different learning styles and should call on the strengths of all your students.

Each activity includes a reproducible student handout and an accompanying teacher page. For each project, be sure to read both the student page and the teacher page before you begin. In most cases, the student handout includes everything students need to get started. The teacher page identifies the basic skills students will use in completing the project, as well as the academic objective for the project.

The teacher material also gives suggestions for the number of students in each group and possible group roles. Some teachers prefer not to assign roles, while some prefer to make sure each student within the group has a specific function and clearly understands what it is. You may use the group roles suggested here or assign other roles to suit the needs of your class.

The suggested group size is also flexible. In many classrooms, two students in a group is often ideal. Students get many of the benefits of group work, but there is less likelihood of one student failing to contribute to the group. However, some of the more complex activities require more students to get the work done. Adjust the group size to fit both your class and the chosen project.

The teacher page also identifies the materials students will need to complete an activity. For many activities where research material is suggested, your U.S. history text may provide enough information to complete the project. Check the text before giving students the handout.

If you think the text gives sufficient coverage, direct students to read the appropriate section of the text instead of doing further research. This will usually mean that they can get started on the project right away.

The suggested procedure included on the teacher page is usually very simple: Distribute copies of the handout, and have students work on the project as directed. Most of the activities are fully explained on the handouts, but you might wish to add some details tailored to the abilities of your own students. For written projects, you may want to assign a certain minimum length. For oral presentations, you might state whether students should speak from complete texts, from notes, or extemporaneously. You may also wish to direct students to include bibliographic references with their written materials. The completed projects can often be used as the springboard for a whole class discussion, or as the basis of a classroom display. For many activities, the procedure also suggests a discussion topic to help students further apply what they have learned.

Since all the activities in this book call for participation from the entire group, it is assumed that each group member will receive the same grade. If this causes friction, or if some group members seem to be coasting and letting the group carry them, you may want to ask for written notes from all group members. You can then decide whether to assign individual grades, a group grade, or a combination.

Several of the activities require students to create maps of the United States that include specific features, so we have included a reproducible outline map on page 131. If you wish, you may give each group a copy of this map along with the activity handout. This makes it easier for students to concentrate on the variable aspects of the map, without having to worry about creating an accurate outline first. This map is listed as optional material for activities where it might be useful.

Once your class has completed an activity, you may find it helpful to keep photocopies of successful work to use as examples the next time you assign the project. For students who find it hard to get started, seeing someone else's approach to the problem can help.

61 Cooperative Learning Activities in U.S. History

TEACHER GUIDE AND REPRODUCIBLE STUDENT PAGES

How the World Was Made

Skills: Research, comprehension, thinking, speaking.

Objectives: Students become familiar with the commonalities and diversity in American societies before European contact.

Project: Comparative chart and oral report.

Suggested Group Roles: Reader, recorder, coordinator, speaker(s).

Suggested Group Size: Three to four students in each group.

Materials Needed: Anthologies of Native American myths and tales to be obtained by students; *How the World Was Made* handout; notebook paper and pens. Optional: creation myths from other parts of the world.

Procedure: Read the Huron creation myth on the handout with the class. If possible, share creation myths from other cultures besides those of North America. Form groups. Students then research other Native American creation myths and prepare charts to compare and contrast stories. Student groups give oral presentations to class.

Evaluation: Does student chart compare at least three Native American creation myths? Do students clearly narrate one myth to the class?

Variations: Have students write their own creation myth. Have students also report on creation myths from other parts of the world.

How the World Was Made

All over the world, people have wondered how the earth was formed and how life began. Many different cultures have stories to explain the beginning of the world. These stories are called creation myths. Each myth tells us something about the people who told it.

The Huron people of North America tell this story about the creation of the world:

> Long ago, the earth was completely covered with water. Only water animals lived there. Then one day a sky woman fell through a rip in the sky and came tumbling toward the water. Two loons caught her as she fell and called loudly to the other animals for help. When Turtle came in answer to their call, the loons placed the woman on Turtle's back. The animals decided that the woman could not live in the water, as they did. They took turns diving down to the bottom o f the sea to bring up some earth for her. At last Toad surfaced with a tiny bit of earth in his mouth. The animals placed the earth on Turtle's shell, and the tiny bit of earth grew, until the whole world was formed.

Early Native American cultures lived in very different parts of the country. Different peoples had different ways of life. They developed many different explanations of the beginning of the world. People of the Plains had a different story than people of the Pacific Northwest did, or people who lived in the forests.

Find creation myths from at least three different Native American peoples. Make a chart listing the stories you find and their essential elements. Include the names of the characters in the stories and what happens to form the world.

Then choose the story the group likes best and present it to the class. You can take turns narrating the story, or each member can take on a different role in the story and act it out for the class.

Native American Peoples

Skills: Research, comprehension, thinking, visual skills.

Objectives: Students learn about the Native American groups who originally lived in their area and combine their information into posters.

Project: Poster based on research.

Suggested Group Roles: Coordinator, recorder, artist, reader, checker.

Suggested Group Size: Four to five students in each group.

Materials Needed: *Native American Peoples* handout; research materials to be obtained by students; poster board or large blank paper; pens, colored pencils, markers. Optional: map showing distribution of Native American peoples before European contact.

Procedure: Distribute handout and discuss with students. Remind students that the Europeans who came to America in the fifteenth and sixteenth centuries didn't come to an empty continent. Many different civilizations flourished here before the first Europeans came. If necessary, help students identify tribes who originally lived in your area. Form groups. Set date for students to complete research and begin group work. Display posters in class.

Evaluation: Do posters include most of the aspects of culture named on the handout? Is the information clearly and attractively presented?

Variations:

1. To form a clearer picture of the diversity among Native American peoples, assign specific tribes or regions to each group.

2. Have student groups make a model of the kind of community Indians in their area would have lived in. The model should show the type of housing most commonly used by this group and how the individual dwellings would be grouped together. The model should also indicate the type of terrain favored by this people. The model could include figures of Native Americans appropriately dressed.

Native American Peoples

Before Europeans came to America, most of the country was occupied by Indians. Although the new settlers soon pushed the Indians off most of their land, traces of Indian life remain in many places.

Find out what Native American people originally lived in your area. Describe their way of life.

- Who were they? What name did they use for themselves?

- Were they hunters? fishers? farmers? a combination?

- What did they hunt? What weapons did they use in hunting?

- What did they grow? What methods of agriculture did they use?

- What kind of homes did they build?

- What building materials did they use?

- What were their beliefs?

- Where did they live?

- Did they have a written language?

- Were any members of this tribe well known?

- What were their clothes like? What materials did they use for clothes?

- Did they live all year in one place, or were they nomadic, moving from place to place?

- What kinds of celebrations did they hold?

- What games and sports did they play?

- What kind of medical treatments and remedies did they have?

- Do any traces of their influence remain in the area?

- Do any local place names have an Indian origin? If so, what do they mean?

Combine all your information into a poster that describes the culture of this people. Illustrate the poster with original drawings and/or photocopies.

1539–1542: La Nueva España

Skills: Map skills, research, thinking, speaking.

Objectives: Students learn about the routes of the Coronado and de Soto expeditions and present dialogues about the expeditions to the class.

Project: Oral dialogue.

Suggested Group Roles: Reader, recorder, speakers.

Suggested Group Size: Two to three students in each group.

Materials Needed: *La Nueva España* handout; research materials to be provided by students; notebook paper and pens.

Procedure: Select groups. Distribute and discuss handout. Students read about the expeditions, then discuss and write their dialogues. Students present their dialogues to the class.

Evaluation: Grade on oral presentation.

Variation: Give students these directions: Trace the route one of these explorers took. Try to imagine what the group members saw along the route and what obstacles they faced. Then prepare a letter a member of the expedition might have written describing to a family member what the group saw. You may either describe one important event or give an overview of the whole trip.

1539–1542: La Nueva España

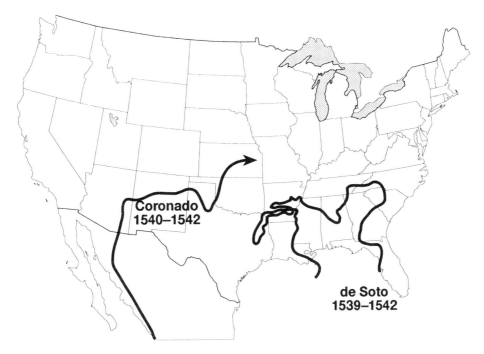

The earliest Europeans to explore North America came from Spain. They hoped to find gold. They also hoped to find a way across America to spice-rich India and China. Hernando de Soto led a party exploring the Southeast. Francisco Coronado led a group through the Southwest. The land they found was different from anything they had ever seen before. It was also different from what they had hoped to find!

The de Soto and Coronado expeditions took place at about the same time. Both crossed into the area now called Texas at some point—Coronado in the northwest, de Soto in the southeast. Imagine they had both continued through Texas and met in the middle. Read more about each expedition. Then create an imaginary dialogue in which the two explorers tell each other what they have seen over the course of their expedition. Present your dialogue to the class.

de Soto: _____

Coronado: _____

de Soto: _____

Coronado: _____

1492–1800's: Who Claimed It First?

Skills: Research, problem solving, map skills.

Objectives: Students understand that many European nations laid claim to America, and determine the dates and extent of European claims.

Project: Map creation.

Suggested Group Roles: Reader, recorder, evaluator, artist.

Suggested Group Size: Three to four students in each group.

Materials Needed: *Who Claimed It First?* handout; notebook paper and pens; blank paper, colored pencils and markers; access to historical atlases. Optional: copies of blank outline map of the United States from page 131.

Procedure: Distribute and discuss handout with students. Form groups and assign roles, if desired. Set date for students to complete their research so that group work can begin. If you wish, you may photocopy and distribute the outline map of the United States from page 131 for students to use. Display completed maps in the classroom.

Teacher Background: Spain—1492–1800's; Portugal—1493–1822; France—1524–1803; Holland—1609–1664; Sweden—1627–1655; Russia—1745–1867; England—1497–1846 in U.S.; still retains ties to Canada.

Evaluation: Do maps include all the countries named on the handout, with accurate dates and areas for each? Is the map neatly and accurately drawn?

Variation: Have students create parallel time lines for each nation's claim on America.

1492–1800's: Who Claimed It First?

We often hear of the Pilgrims as if they were the first Europeans to come to the Americas. In fact, these English settlers were relatively late arrivals. Several other countries had already claimed land in America.

Investigate the history of European claims in America. When did each of these nations first claim part of America? What area did it claim? How long did its claim last? Do we see any traces of that claim today?

Once you have all the information, use it to create a map of both North America and South America that shows European claims. One approach would be to use a different color for each country. Remember to include both a key and a caption for your map. These are some of the European nations that claimed parts of America:

Spain: _____

_____

Portugal: _____

_____

France: _____

_____

Holland: _____

_____

Sweden: _____

_____

England: _____

_____

Russia: _____

_____

1620: In Other Words

Skills: Reading, comprehension, writing.

Objectives: Students understand one of the earliest American manifestations of the principle that government should be based on the consent of the governed.

Project: Paraphrasing a paragraph.

Suggested Group Roles: Reader, recorder, checker.

Suggested Group Size: Three to four students in each group.

Materials Needed: *In Other Words* handout; classroom set of dictionaries; notebook paper and pens.

Procedure: Form groups. Distribute and discuss handout. Discuss what primary source documents are. Students work in class to paraphrase the document. After students have completed work on the handout, discuss the importance of the Mayflower Compact.

Teacher Background: The Mayflower Compact was the first manifestation of a basic American principle: that government should be based on the consent of the governed.

Evaluation: Did students accurately paraphrase the Mayflower Compact?

Variations:

1. Have students include a sentence or two—in their own words—explaining the importance of the Mayflower Compact.

2. Have students role-play different members of the *Mayflower's* complement and discuss the pros and cons of developing something like the Mayflower Compact.

1620: In Other Words

Before the first colonists on the *Mayflower* landed in what is now Massachusetts, they agreed to obey the rules set by the group. This agreement is known as the Mayflower Compact.

> We whose names are underwritten, . . . having undertaken for the glory of God, and advancement of the Christian faith and honor of our king and country, a voyage to plant the first colony in the northern parts of Virginia, do by these presents solemnly and mutually, in the presence of God and one of another, covenant and combine ourselves together into a civil body politic, for our better ordering and preservation and further-ance of the end aforesaid; and by virtue hereof to enact, constitute, and frame such just and equal laws, ordinances, acts, constitutions, and offices from time to time as shall be thought most meet and convenient for the general good of the colony; unto which we promise all due submission and obedience.

The language used in this document is similar to the English we use today. Still, it isn't very clear to a modern reader. Write out the meaning of the excerpt in your own words. Use a dictionary for words you don't know.

1659: Fire, Fire!

Skills: Problem solving, visual skills.

Objectives: Students explore some of the challenges faced by colonists in America.

Project: Drawing.

Suggested Group Roles: Recorder, artist.

Suggested Group Size: Two to four students in each group.

Materials Needed: *Fire, Fire!* handout; blank paper; pens, markers, colored pencils.

Procedure: Distribute and discuss handout with students. Form groups and have students work as the handout directs. Display completed drawings in the classroom.

Evaluation: Grade on neatness and completeness of drawings. Drawing should include the following essential details: wheels, so the fire engine can be moved from place to place; a water tank or reservoir; some kind of pumping mechanism, to get the water from the reservoir; and a hose or syringe of some kind to direct the water onto the fire.

1659: Fire, Fire!

In colonial times, many buildings were made entirely of wood. Most heating and cooking were done using open fires. In towns and cities, buildings were often very close to each other. These factors added up to a severe fire danger.

A chimney fire in one house could send a rain of sparks onto the houses near it. Within minutes, a whole street could be on fire.

The only way to fight fires was using a "bucket brigade." As many people as possible formed a line from a pump or pond to the burning building. The person nearest the water filled a bucket and passed it to the next person. Each bucket went from hand to hand until it reached the person nearest the fire. That person threw the water on the fire, then passed the empty bucket back to be refilled. Needless to say, a lot of buildings burned down completely before the fire could be put out this way.

In 1659, Joseph Jencks, an ironworker, built the first "fire engine" in America. It was a portable water pump with a self-contained water supply. Imagine a fire and people's reactions when this fire engine rolled onto the scene to supplement the bucket brigade.

Talk about what you think Jencks's invention might have looked like. Then make a drawing of Jencks's fire engine. If you like, you can show the fire engine being used at a fire.

1680's: Coastal Cities

Skills: Research, thinking, writing, map skills.

Objectives: Students learn about early European colonization and the influence of geography on patterns of settlement.

Project: Written history.

Suggested Group Roles: Reader, recorder, evaluator, artist (optional).

Suggested Group Size: Three to four students in each group.

Materials Needed: *Coastal Cities* handout; notebook paper and pens; research materials to be obtained by students.

Procedure: Distribute and discuss handout with students. Form groups, and set dates for planning in class, research outside of class, and final preparation in class. After students have completed the work described on the handout, use the results to discuss the influence of geography on early settlement patterns.

Evaluation: Grade on completeness and accuracy of written work.

Variations:

1. Present this idea to students: While the east coast of North America is speckled with bays and harbors, the west coast is comparatively smooth. If the first foreign settlers had landed on the west coast, instead of on the east, how might the different topography there have affected the development of a colony?

2. Have students make a model of the city, based on their research. The model should show the coastline immediately north and south of the city, the relationship of the city to the river and any other nearby bodies of water, and any other important physical features in the area.

1680's: Coastal Cities

When European settlers began to found colonies in North America, they tended to settle along the coast. This made it easier for them to get supplies from home than if they had to move goods overland. It was also easier to ship goods back to Europe.

Of course, access to the ocean wasn't the only thing colonists wanted in a site to settle. They wanted plenty of fresh water to drink, and an easy way to explore inland, too. Because of this, many settlements were started where a river joined the sea. These settlements included Boston, New York, Baltimore, Charleston, and Philadelphia.

Choose one of these cities and find out as much as you can about its history. Here are some questions you might ask to get you started:

- What river is the city on?

- When was the city founded?

- Who first settled it?

- Did it act as a major port for the area around it?

- Were any important cities founded farther up the river, so that they depended on the port city's harbor?

- What kind of goods were shipped through the port?

- When was the city at its richest?

- What is the city best known for?

- What was its population in the 1680's?

- What is its population today?

Use the information you find to write a brief history of this city in the late 1600's. Include as much information as you can. If you wish, you can include a map showing the city in relation to the coast and inland area.

1650–1750: Indentured Servants

Skills: Comprehension, thinking, speaking.

Objectives: Students learn about the economy and labor systems of the early colonies.

Project: Oral conversation.

Suggested Group Roles: Recorder, coordinator, checker.

Suggested Group Size: Four to five students in each group.

Materials Needed: *Indentured Servants* handout; notebook paper and pens.

Procedure: Distribute and discuss handout with students. Form groups and have students work as the handout directs. Students perform conversations for the class.

Evaluation: Grade on accuracy and oral presentation.

1650–1750: Indentured Servants

Most people who came to the early American colonies wanted to be independent. They bought land or set up in business for themselves. This meant that employers found it hard to hire servants or laborers. Most people were working for themselves.

One answer to this problem was found in "indentured servants." These were people who agreed to work in America for a certain number of years. In return, their employer paid for their trip from Europe to the colonies.

Some indentured servants were treated very well. When their time of service was up, their employers gave them tools, seed, and sometimes even land so that they could set up for themselves.

Some servants weren't treated as kindly. Indentured servants could be bought and sold like property. They could not get married without their master's permission. They could not work for someone else. They often had to work very hard and were not fed well.

Some masters branded their indentured servants. Then, if the servants ran away, they were easy to identify. Indentured servants hired out to bad masters often didn't live until the end of their period of service.

Develop a conversation among a group of indentured servants. One, who had a kind master, has just completed her term of service. One has just arrived from Europe and is finding everything in this new life very strange. Decide on the situation of the other servants among yourselves. Then write a conversation among these servants talking about their experiences. The conversation should include telling the recent arrival what to expect in this new life and discussing the future plans of the newly freed woman. Perform your conversation for the class.

1700: The U.S. Mail

Skills: Problem solving, writing, map skills.

Objectives: Students gain understanding of how difficult communication between England and the colonies was.

Project: Written description with optional map.

Suggested Group Roles: Recorder, checker.

Suggested Group Size: Two to three students in each group.

Materials Needed: *The U.S. Mail* handout; notebook paper and pens; blank paper, markers, colored pencils.

Procedure: Distribute and discuss handout with students. Form groups and have students work as the handout directs.

Evaluation: Grade written work on creativity and reasonableness of suggested route, and (optional) accuracy and neatness of map.

1700: The U.S. Mail

Most people in America take the postal system for granted. We're all used to a central system for delivering mail. But in the early days of the colonies, there was no such central system.

The colonial postal system was created in 1691. It wasn't very reliable. To send a letter, you just folded it over, sealed it with wax, and gave it to a stagecoach driver. Instead of paying to send a letter, people paid to receive them. The postage depended on how many miles the letter had to travel. To receive the letter, the addressee had to go to his or her local post office and pay the charges.

To make sure their letters arrived, people often sent two or three copies of the same letter, by different routes. Even then, there was no guarantee that any of them would be received. Letters from one country to another were very uncertain. It was hard for people in the colonies to stay in touch with their families in Europe.

Using your imagination and your knowledge of the period, describe a possible scenario for a letter. It was sent from a woman in Kent, England, to her daughter in the colonies in 1700. Write an account of the journey the letter might take, and the people who might handle it. If you wish, you could include a map showing the letter's route.

1704: The Boston Post Road

Skills: Research, comprehension, writing.

Objectives: Students understand the difficulties in moving from place to place in the colonies. They also see how human action has changed the physical environment by the building of roads and highways.

Project: Written first-person account.

Suggested Group Roles: Reader, recorder.

Suggested Group Size: Two to three students in each group.

Materials Needed: *The Boston Post Road* handout; notebook paper and pens; research materials to be provided by students.

Procedure: Distribute and discuss handout with students. Form groups and have students work as the handout directs.

Evaluation: Grade on completeness of written work.

Variations:

1. Have student groups research the road as Knight might have found it, then illustrate one aspect of her trip.

2. Have students make a map or model of the Boston Post Road as it might have appeared to the travelers in the early 1700's.

1704: The Boston Post Road

The United States today has an excellent system of roads. Broad, well-maintained highways run between our cities. They are marked with signs that can even be read at night. In cities and towns, most streets are paved, well-marked, and bright with electric lighting.

In colonial times, there were very few roads. Often, the roads between towns were only trails. They were widened by travel, but not graded or paved. When a road came to a river, travelers usually had to cross the river by fording it, or walking through at a shallow place. There were few bridges or ferries. Even when stagecoaches, toll bridges, and toll ferries were introduced around 1750, it took three days, traveling all day and part of each night, to go from Boston to Philadelphia.

The Boston Post Road was one of the earliest colonial roads. In 1704 Sarah Kemble Knight, a Boston schoolteacher, went on horseback from Boston to New York by the Boston Post Road. When she came to rivers too deep to ford, she swam her horse across. She was ferried across the river at Providence in a canoe. Although she traveled from dawn to dark, it took her seven days to travel 200 miles.

Find out as much as you can about roads and travel in America in 1704, including the inns and taverns a traveler might stay in. Then write a first-person account of Sarah Knight's trip.

1763: Start Your Own Business

Skills: Research, problem solving, writing, visual skills.

Objectives: Students investigate some of the economic factors that contributed to the colonists' desire for independence.

Project: Written business proposal.

Suggested Group Roles: Reader, recorder, checker.

Suggested Group Size: Two to three students in each group.

Materials Needed: *Start Your Own Business* handout; notebook paper and pens; research materials to be provided by students.

Procedure: Discuss the Navigation Acts of 1651. Distribute handouts. Form groups and have students work as the handout directs.

Teacher Background: Under the Navigation Acts of 1651, colonists could only sell their goods to foreigners if the goods were shipped through English ports and on English or colonial ships. Other laws said that some colonial products—including tobacco, sugar, wool, and furs—could only be sold in England. Also, certain goods could only be legally manufactured in the colonies on a limited scale. These included hats, linens, woolens, and iron products.

Evaluation: Grade written work on completeness and accuracy.

1763: Start Your Own Business

In its dealings with the colonies, England—naturally enough—was trying to get rich, while also trying to keep other countries from getting rich. England set up rules to make sure that no other nation would benefit from the American colonies. Among other things, the colonies were not allowed to make things that would compete with goods made in England. Trade between the colonies and other countries was strictly limited.

The year is 1763. With some fellow colonists, you want to start a small manufacturing business. You know that a lot of people just ignore the laws about what things can be manufactured in the colonies and how goods can be sold to other countries. But you really want to do things the right way.

Investigate to see what goods you can legally make and what goods you can't. Also, find out what you have to do to export the things you make. Then choose one item in common use in the 1760's as the product you will make.

Write up a proposal for your business. Describe what you have chosen to make and how you plan to sell it. Include information about whether you can only sell your product within the American colonies or whether you can export it to other countries. If you wish, you can illustrate your proposal with a drawing of your product.

1765: The Raid on Hutchinson's House

Skills: Research, thinking, writing.

Objectives: Students explore some of the factors leading to the revolutionary movement in the American colonies.

Project: Written eyewitness account.

Suggested Group Roles: Reader, recorder, evaluator.

Suggested group size: Three to four students in each group.

Materials needed: *The Raid on Hutchinson's House* handout; notebook paper and pens; research material to be provided by students.

Procedure: Form groups. Distribute and discuss handout with students. Set date for students to have materials in class and work in groups to begin.

Evaluation: Grade written work on accuracy and creativity.

Variations:

1. Have students create an illustration of the attack.

2. Have students create a conversation in which two or three people who took part in the attack describe what happened.

1765: The Raid on Hutchinson's House

In 1765, Britain imposed a Stamp Act on the American colonies. It said that people had to pay for a certain kind of stamp that was put on most printed materials. This act didn't seem very radical in Britain. People there had paid a similar tax for a long time.

In the American colonies, this act made many people angry. Organizations called the Sons of Liberty were formed. They made bonfires of the stamps and threatened the people who were supposed to collect the fees for the stamps. The Sons of Liberty held anti-Stamp Act rallies and parades. A mob in Boston attacked the home of Lieutenant Governor Thomas Hutchinson, destroying everything of value in the house.

Find out as much as you can about people's attitudes toward the Stamp Act and the way they acted to protest against it. Get as many details as possible about the attack on Hutchinson's house. Then write an eyewitness account of the attack, as told by a 13-year-old who got caught up in the mob.

Here are some questions you might ask:

- What date was the attack?

- How did the mob form?

- At what time did the attack take place?

- Did the mob go for the front of the house, the back of the house, or both?

- How long did the raid last?

- How did it end?

- What did the mob do afterwards?

- What happened to the people who lived in the house?

- What happened to the house and the things in it?

- What was Governor Hutchinson's reaction?

- How did the 13-year-old narrator get caught up in the mob?

- What did the narrator think of the whole event?

1770: The Boston Massacre

Skills: Research, problem solving, visual skills.

Objectives: Students see how activists manipulated events to promote colonial desire for independence.

Project: Drawing/painting.

Suggested Group Roles: Reader, recorder, artist.

Suggested Group Size: Two to three students in each group.

Materials Needed: *The Boston Massacre* handout; copy of Paul Revere engraving "The Boston Massacre" (in many U.S. history textbooks); research materials to be provided by students.

Procedure: Distribute handout. Show students the Paul Revere engraving, and discuss its inaccuracies. Then form groups and have students work as the handout directs. Display completed drawings in the classroom.

Evaluation: Grade drawings on accuracy and originality.

1770: The Boston Massacre

On March 5, 1770, a group of men and boys started to heckle a squad of British soldiers in Boston. The Bostonians resented having British troops in their city. They started to throw rocks and snowballs.

Without orders, some soldiers opened fire on the mob. Three people were killed right away and eight were wounded. Two of the wounded people later died.

Many colonists formed their opinion of this event from an engraving by Paul Revere. His picture wasn't very accurate, but it was excellent propaganda. It helped to form a strong anti-British feeling among colonists. It also helped increase the demand for independence.

Read any other accounts of the Boston Massacre you can find. Using that information, and the account given here, create your own version of Revere's print. Include as many actual details of the architecture shown in Revere's engraving as you can, but give a more truthful account of the event.

1775: Samuel Prescott's Ride

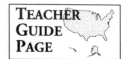

Skills: Problem solving, writing, speaking.

Objectives: Students learn that historians must be selective in their use of material, and that well-known "facts" can sometimes be fiction.

Project: Oral delivery of original poem.

Suggested Group Roles: Reader, recorder, speaker.

Suggested Group Size: Two to three students in each group.

Materials Needed: *Samuel Prescott's Ride* handout; copy of "Paul Revere's Ride" by Henry Wadsworth Longfellow; notebook paper and pens.

Procedure: Read to students the poem "Paul Revere's Ride." Distribute handout and discuss with students. Form groups and have students work as the handout directs. Groups read poems to the class.

Evaluation: Grade on accuracy and originality.

Variations:

1. All three of the riders were dead before Longfellow wrote his poem. Imagine that they were alive—and that the other two men were angry because Revere got all the glory and they weren't even mentioned. Write a letter from William Dawes and Samuel Prescott to Henry Wadsworth Longfellow, pointing out his mistake.

2. Have students compose a ballad or other song to memorialize Samuel Prescott's ride. If they wish, students can set their words to an existing song.

1775: Samuel Prescott's Ride

Listen, my children, and you shall hear
Of the midnight ride of Paul Revere.

These are the opening lines of a poem written by Henry Wadsworth Longfellow in 1863. The poem tells the story of Paul Revere's ride to warn the colonists that the British were coming. The poem was very popular and made Paul Revere's name famous.

It was also quite untrue. Yes, Paul Revere did start out on that ride, along with two other men, William Dawes and Samuel Prescott. But Revere didn't get all the way to Concord. He was captured near Lexington.

William Dawes also reached Lexington and went on to ride to Concord. Revere warned him about the British patrols. Dawes turned back.

Samuel Prescott, a young doctor, continued the ride. He managed to avoid the patrols and rode all the way to Concord with his warning.

Write a poem describing what really happened that night in April 1775. You can use your imagination to add details and atmosphere, but don't get carried away—as Henry Longfellow did! Read your poem to the class.

1776: Slaves in the New Nation

Skills: Research, thinking, visual skills.

Objectives: Students investigate how the Revolution affected—or didn't affect—different segments of American society.

Project: Time line.

Suggested Group Roles: Reader, recorder, artist.

Suggested Group Size: Two to three students in each group.

Materials Needed: *Slaves in the New Nation* handout; notebook paper and pens; blank paper, colored pencils, markers.

Procedure: Distribute handout. Discuss time line preparation. Form groups and have students work as the handout directs. Display completed time lines in the classroom.

Evaluation: Did students include at least 15 entries on their time lines? Did they include both real and imagined, but possible, events? Is the time line neatly executed?

Variation: Ask students to read "all men" as "all people"—men and women. How would American history have been changed?

1776: Slaves in the New Nation

Although Thomas Jefferson owned slaves, he wasn't sure that this was right. When he wrote the Declaration of Independence, he apparently decided that slavery was wrong. He included a section in his first draft of the Declaration that condemned the English king for crimes against Africans, "a distant people who never offended him, captivating & carrying them into slavery in another hemisphere, or to incur miserable death in their transportation hither."

When the rest of the committee working on the Declaration read this, they insisted on taking it out. So when the colonies finally signed a document saying, "All men are created equal," they deliberately left out a large part of the population of America.

Imagine how the United States might have developed if those influential men had decided that "all men" really meant all men—regardless of color or national origin. Create a time line for this imaginary United States.

Your time line should include at least 15 important entries. Choose a scale that relates to the entries chosen. If most of your entries took place between 1776 and 1810, you would use a large scale. For example, you might make 3 inches on your time line represent 10 years. If you plan to include entries from 1776 to the 1990's, you would use a smaller scale. For example, you might make half an inch represent 15 years.

Spread your entries out across the entire time line. Avoid having 8 or 10 entries within a few years of each other, with the remaining entries spread out over centuries. Make sure the spaces between entries are in proper proportion—a 50-year gap should be much wider than a 5-year gap. Start with the freeing of all slaves at the end of the Revolutionary War. Include some real events on your time line, events that would have happened anyway, as well as imagined events. You can use this sheet to start your notes.

(continued)

1776: Slaves in the New Nation *(continued)*

Historical events that would probably have happened anyway:

_____   _____

_____   _____

Historical events that would probably have changed:

_____   _____

_____   _____

Events that might not have happened:

_____   _____

_____   _____

Events that might have happened instead:

_____   _____

_____   _____

1781: The Articles of Confederation

Skills: Problem solving, writing.

Objectives: Students consider the challenges of creating a government, at both national and state levels.

Project: Chart.

Suggested Group Roles: Reader, recorder, checker, evaluator.

Suggested Group Size: Three to four students in each group.

Materials Needed: *The Articles of Confederation* handout; notebook paper and pens; blank paper, colored pencils, markers.

Procedure: Distribute and discuss handout with students. Form groups and have students work as the handout directs. Display completed charts in the classroom.

Evaluation: Grade on neatness and completeness.

Special Tips: This activity should be done before studying the Articles of Confederation, to help students understand some of the problems the new nation faced.

1781: The Articles of Confederation

After the Revolution, the new nation needed a plan for government. This presented problems. Almost the only thing the 13 colonies had in common was wanting to be free from England. Each colony had a different economy. Most had different interests and different attitudes toward government. They were almost like 13 separate countries. They needed to have some sort of central direction while letting each state make many of its own laws.

Your group has been given the job of coming up with a plan for governing the new country. Your plan should give each state some freedom but let the nation act as one country as well.

Here are some questions to get you started:

- What kind of rights should be guaranteed to the states? to individuals within the states?

- What kind of duties and responsibilities should states have to each other? to the nation as a whole?

- What should be the relationship of the states to each other? to the central government?

Make a chart to present your plan. Your chart should show: the relationships between the states and the nation; the relationships between the states and the individual; the relationships between the nation and the individual; the relationships between states.

1785: The State of Franklin

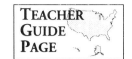

Skills: Thinking, problem solving, writing, visual skills.

Objectives: Students learn about some of the issues and frictions involved in creating a new state.

Project: Written TV plot outline.

Suggested Group Roles: Artist, recorder, reader, checker.

Suggested Group Size: Four to five students in each group.

Materials Needed: *The State of Franklin* handout; notebook paper and pens; blank paper, markers, colored pencils.

Procedure: Distribute and discuss handout with students. Form groups and have students work as the handout directs. After the work has been completed, discuss what the Franklinite action tells students about attitudes toward unity after the Revolution.

Evaluation: Grade written work on completeness and originality.

Variations:

1. Students write the opening scene for the pilot and act it out for the class. If a video camera is available, students can videotape the scene.

2. Have students make a map of the United States today as it might have looked if the disputes between the states after the Revolution had not been resolved. Students should decide who would have kept control of the disputed areas and whether or not those areas would be separate states today.

1785: The State of Franklin

After the Revolution, several states had claims on western territory. Sometimes, more than one state claimed the same area. To settle their disagreements, several states offered to give their western territory to the federal government.

North Carolina offered the U.S. government part of the area now known as Tennessee. But the settlers in the area along the Watauga River didn't like the idea. They were annoyed that North Carolina would transfer their land without their consent. They held several conventions and then, in 1785, established the new state of Franklin. The Franklinites elected a governor—John Sevier, a prominent militia leader and land speculator. They also filled a number of other offices.

Both Congress and North Carolina refused to recognize the new state. By 1788, it no longer existed. In 1789, North Carolina ceded the territory to the federal government. In 1796, Tennessee became a state and was admitted to the Union.

You have been asked to prepare a pilot for a TV show set in the state of Franklin in the 1780's. The series will eventually give the entire history of the short-lived state, with fictional episodes set against the historical background. The pilot will set the scene for the whole series. It should be set in Franklin, but some scenes can take place elsewhere. Who will be the main characters in your series? What part of the history of Franklin will you give in the pilot, and what will you save for later episodes?

Write an outline for the plot of the first episode. Name the characters, and say where each scene takes place. If you like, you can give detailed descriptions of the scenes, or you can make drawings to show the different settings.

1789: King George I

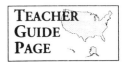

Skills: Problem solving, writing.

Objectives: Students learn about the development of new political institutions in the United States.

Project: Written description of hypothetical event.

Suggested Group Roles: Reader, recorder, checker.

Suggested Group Size: Two to three students in each group.

Materials Needed: *King George I* handout; notebook paper and pens.

Procedure: Distribute and discuss handout with students. Form groups and have students work as the handout directs.

Evaluation: Grade on creativity and writing skills.

Variations:

1. Have students prepare a skit acting out an argument between advocates of a U.S. monarchy and those in favor of a republic.

2. Have students create an illustration of the coronation of King George I of America.

3. Have students imagine what TV coverage of King George Washington's coronation would have been like. Students can then role-play a TV newscast describing the ceremony.

1789: King George I

In the late 1700's, most countries were ruled by kings or emperors. Only a few small countries like Holland and Switzerland had republics, where government was based on the consent of the people.

Most Americans were used to being ruled by a king. They didn't rebel against England to get rid of the king. They rebelled because they wanted a government that took their needs into account.

Some people assumed that, after the Revolution, the former American colonies would set up their own monarchy. A group of George Washington's soldiers wanted to make him king of America!

Imagine what America would have been like if George Washington had become king, not president.

Here are some questions to get you started:

- Where would King George's coronation have taken place?

- Who would have crowned George king?

- Would America have had a hereditary monarchy?

- If so, who would have succeeded George I, since he had no children of his own?

- If America would not have had a hereditary monarchy, how would the next king have been chosen?

Write a description of King George's coronation. Include an explanation of the kind of monarchy we might have had.

1780's: Money, Money

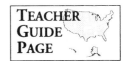

Skills: Research, writing, visual skills.

Objectives: Students explore some of the economic problems facing the new nation.

Project: Illustrated written report.

Suggested Group Roles: Reader, recorder, artist.

Suggested Group Size: Two to three students in each group.

Materials Needed: *Money, Money* handout; notebook paper and pens; blank paper, markers, colored pencils. Research materials to be provided by students.

Procedure: Decide how long you wish the student report to be. Distribute handout and discuss with students. Form groups and have students work as directed in the handout.

Teacher Background: Part of the reason for the shortage of specie after the Revolution lay in the fact that England did not furnish coins to the colonies and forbade the colonies to make them. To simplify trade, the colonists used any foreign coins they could get—English shillings, Spanish dollars, French and Dutch coins. The large Spanish silver dollars, called *pieces of eight*, were popular. They were often cut into eight pie-shaped pieces to make change. Two bits of the original coin were worth a quarter of a dollar, four bits were half a dollar, etc. Despite the ban, the colonies did produce some coins and bills. Massachusetts produced several silver coins, including a pine-tree shilling and an oak-tree shilling.

You might compare the situation in the colonies with that in Italy during the 1980's and 1990's, when the country had a shortage of change. When change was required after making a purchase, shopkeepers often gave the purchaser small pieces of candy to make up the difference, as they had no coins.

Evaluation: Grade on completeness and accuracy, and good execution of the illustrations.

Variations:

1. Have students create pieces of eight from paper, then act out a transaction that involves buying something with these coins and making change.

2. Ask students to imagine what it would be like to live in an economy that had goods but no currency. Have them brainstorm other ways of doing business besides using money as a medium of exchange.

1780's: Money, Money

After the Revolution, most Americans hoped to put the war behind them and return to normal life. But the new country faced a lot of problems. One of them was money.

In the 1700's, paper money was meant to be a convenience. A paper note represented a certain amount of gold or silver. Before a state printed money, it was supposed to have enough gold or silver to back the paper money. If a state printed 100 dollar bills, it had to have 100 dollars' worth of gold.

But in the years after the Revolution, both the federal government and individual states often printed money without enough gold to back up the paper. They might print 200 dollars when they only had 100 dollars' worth of gold.

Merchants, and people who were owed money, grew unwilling to accept paper money. They wanted coins. But there weren't many coins in circulation!

Find out as much as you can about the money circulating in the years after the Revolution.

Here are some questions you might ask to get you started:

- Who printed paper money?

- In what denominations?

- What coins were in circulation?

- What were the names of the coins?

- How much were they worth?

- Where did they come from?

- Were coins always worth the value stamped on them?

Write a report on American currency in the years soon after the Revolution. Illustrate your report with drawings or photocopies of coins and bills from this period.

1785–1820: The Buildings of a Nation

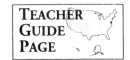

Skills: Research, thinking, visual skills.

Objectives: Students see how the political ideals of the new nation were embodied in architecture.

Project: Poster.

Suggested Group Roles: Artist, reader, recorder.

Suggested Group Size: Two to three students per group.

Materials Needed: *The Buildings of a Nation* handout; notebook paper and pens; poster board or large blank paper; colored pencils and markers.

Procedure: Distribute handout and discuss with students. Form groups. Set date for students to complete research and begin group work in class. Display completed posters in classroom.

Evaluation: Grade on completeness and quality of posters.

Variation: Some groups might want to try making a model of a Federal-style building. As this would be more complex than making a poster, the group size for such a project should be larger. Stiff paper or light card are effective for making a model of this type.

1785–1820: The Buildings of a Nation

When people put up buildings, they often have more in mind than just providing shelter. Otherwise the world would be full of simple buildings designed only to keep the weather out.

Instead, people everywhere use their buildings to express things. A building can show the builder's interests and attitudes. It can show the influence of other cultures. It can be designed to fit into a landscape, or to stand out from it.

Often, many buildings put up around the same time have things in common. When we look at these buildings today, we can say that buildings with a lot of features in common are built in a specific style. Some well-known housing styles include Elizabethan, Queen Anne, Tudor, and Victorian—all named after kings and queens of England.

Before the American Revolution, the most common architectural style in the English colonies was called Georgian, after King George of England. After the Revolution, a popular style in America was known as Federal. This style was named after the new federation of states, instead of after a king or queen.

Find out as much as you can about the Federal style. What were the typical features of this style? What kinds of buildings was it used for? Do many examples of this building style exist today? Are there any in the area where you live?

Make a poster showing a typical Federal-style building. Include as many of the important features of this architectural style as you can. Label each special feature on the poster. At the bottom of the poster, include a brief description of the Federal style.

       61 Cooperative Learning Activities in U.S. History

1800: Capital Soap Opera

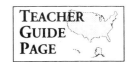

Skills: Research, thinking, writing, speaking.

Objectives: Students recognize that political democracy in the early republic was fluid and that many of today's political institutions evolved out of early conflicts.

Project: Soap opera written and performed.

Suggested Group Roles: Reader, recorder, coordinator, checker.

Suggested Group Size: Four to five students in each group.

Materials Needed: *Capital Soap Opera* handout; notebook paper and pens.

Procedure: Distribute handout and discuss with students. Form groups. If your U.S. history textbook provides a good description of events during and after the election of 1800, direct students to read the relevant material in their texts. Otherwise, set a date for students to complete research and begin group work in class as directed in the handout. Groups perform scenes for the class. If a video camera is available, you may wish to videotape student presentations.

Evaluation: Grade on oral presentation, basic accuracy of written work, and dramatic creativity.

1800: Capital Soap Opera

Suspense . . . intrigue . . . scandal . . . wild accusations . . . a fatal duel. It sounds like an excerpt from a soap opera, but it's actually a description of events in the election of 1800.

These are some of the key people involved in this election:

- Thomas Jefferson

- Aaron Burr

- John Adams

- Charles C. Pinckney

- Alexander Hamilton

Research the election of 1800. Find out what the fuss was all about and what happened to these people afterwards. Then write an account of the election as it might appear on a TV soap opera. Keep the basic facts, but feel free to exaggerate for effect.

Here are some questions you might want to ask:

- What were the "midnight appointments"?

- Why did Burr and Hamilton fight a duel in 1804?

- What did Congress do to prevent another election like this one?

- How many times did the House of Representatives vote before reaching a decision?

- How close was the inauguration when a president was finally chosen?

Perform one scene from your soap opera in front of the class.

1804: In the Footsteps of Lewis and Clark

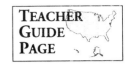

Skills: Map skills, problem solving.

Objectives: Students relate U.S. territorial expansion in the early 1800's to their own geographic context today.

Project: Trip plan.

Suggested Group Roles: Recorder, artist.

Suggested Group Size: Two students in each group.

Materials Needed: *In the Footsteps of Lewis and Clark* handout; notebook paper and pens; blank paper, colored pencils, markers; travel information to be provided by students. Optional: blank outline map of the United States from page 131.

Procedure: Distribute handout and discuss with students. Form groups. Set date for students to complete research and begin group work in class. If you wish, distribute outline map of the United States from page 131 for students to use. Display completed maps in classroom. After maps are completed, discuss how the country has changed since the days of Lewis and Clark; the trip that took them over two years to complete can now be made in days—hours if you fly!

Evaluation: Grade maps on accuracy and completeness.

Variation: Have different groups research how to get to a particular destination by road, by rail, by bus, etc.

Special Tips: Travel agents can provide helpful information about how to get to places, what to see when there, where to stay, and so on. The American Automobile Association offers members help with planning routes. A letter to the Chamber of Commerce of the chosen destination could provide helpful brochures and information about nearby attractions.

Name _____   Date _____

1804: In the Footsteps of Lewis and Clark

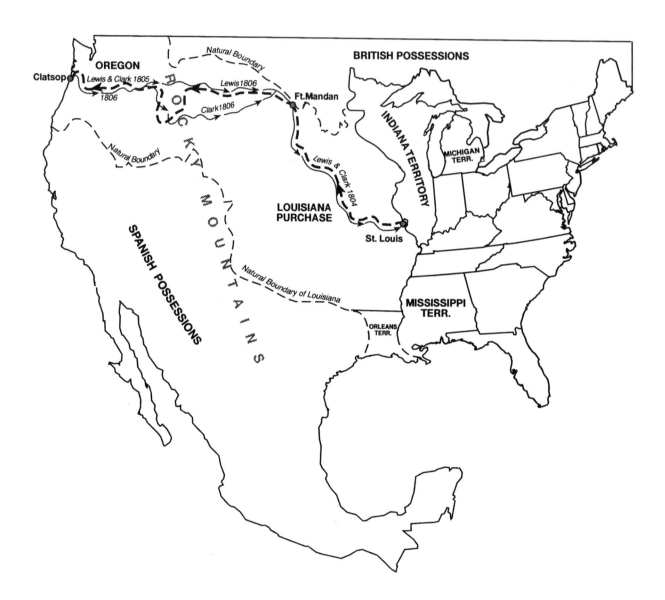

Route of the Lewis and Clark Expedition, 1804–1806

(continued)

1804: In the Footsteps of Lewis and Clark
(continued)

In 1803, the United States bought the Louisiana Territory from France. The purchase added more than 825,000 square miles of land to the young country.

However, some of the boundaries of the new territory were vague, and most of the land was uncharted. In 1804, Meriwether Lewis and William Clark set off from St. Louis to explore the new territory.

Compare this map of their route with a map of America today. Choose one place that the Lewis and Clark expedition passed through, and plan a trip to it—using today's methods of transportation, not those of Lewis and Clark! Create a map to show the itinerary for your trip. The map should include your starting point (your home) and your destination, and as much other information about the route as you can find.

Here are some questions to get you started:

- Will you drive, fly, go by train, or go by bus?

- What U.S. highways go to your destination point?

- What railway lines go to your destination?

- Is there an airport either at your destination or nearby?

- Are there any points of interest near your destination? How far away are they? How would you get to them? Are any of them related to Lewis and Clark?

- Where will you stay on your trip? What hotels, motels, or campgrounds are available?

1812: Steam Power

Skills: Research, thinking, writing.

Objectives: Students investigate how technological developments affected regional and economic development in areas linked by the Mississippi River.

Project: Written account.

Suggested Group Roles: Reader, recorder, checker.

Suggested Group Size: Two to three students in each group.

Materials Needed: *Steam Power* handout; notebook paper and pens; research materials to be provided by students.

Procedure: Distribute handout and discuss with students. Form groups. Set date for students to complete research and begin group work in class.

Teacher Background: By the 1820's, the steamboat had linked the American interior with the South and the East Coast via the Mississippi River and the Gulf of Mexico.

Evaluation: Grade written work on completeness and originality.

Variation: Have students create a model or a detailed drawing of an early steamboat. The model or drawing should show the features that made the steamboat design so successful, including the wide, shallow shape that enabled it to negotiate uncertain waters.

1812: Steam Power

In 1807, Robert Fulton launched his steamboat *Clermont*. It was the first commercially successful steam-powered boat.

Just four years later, in 1811, Fulton's steamboat *New Orleans* was launched in Pittsburgh. It took 14 days to go downriver from Pittsburgh to New Orleans.

The steamboat *New Orleans* reached the city of New Orleans in January 1812. It was the first steamboat to sail down the Mississippi River. It caused a sensation. The boat soon began to make a regular run from New Orleans to Natchez. The cost was $18 for the trip downstream and $25 for the trip upstream.

Learn as much as you can about transportation on the Mississippi River, and why it was so important. Then write an account of this first trip from the captain's point of view. Include as much information about the importance of the river as you can.

Here are some questions to get you started:

• How far was it from Natchez to New Orleans? _____

_____

• Why did it cost more to go upriver than down? _____

_____

• What other rivers connected to the Mississippi? _____

_____

• What cities or areas could be connected by travel on the Mississippi? _____

_____

1818: Tinned Food

Skills: Problem solving, visual skills.

Objectives: Students explore how American industrialization affected markets and individuals.

Project: Marketing plan.

Suggested Group Roles: Recorder, artist.

Suggested Group Size: Two to three students in each group.

Materials Needed: *Tinned Food* handout; notebook paper and pens; blank paper, markers, colored pencils.

Procedure: Distribute handout and discuss with students. Form groups and have students work as directed in the handout. Display completed ads and labels in the classroom.

Evaluation: Grade work on completeness and originality.

Variation: Have one group design a poster, one design labels, etc. Combine all the individual products in a group display.

1818: Tinned Food

In 1818, an Englishman named Peter Durand introduced tinned food in America. Before this, people had few ways of keeping food fresh. Some vegetables could be kept in root cellars through the winter. Fruit could be preserved in syrup or as jam. Some foods could be kept by pickling them in salty water, or brine. Some meats could be smoked or dried. But the methods we use most today—refrigerating and canning in metal tins—were not available before 1818.

You have gone into business with Durand to sell tinned food in America. What might make it hard to introduce this new approach to preserving food? How will you convince people that tinned food is safe? that it is nutritious? that it is convenient?

Develop a marketing plan to convince people to buy your product. You will advertise this new method of packaging food with posters on billboards and through ads in newspapers. Design labels to put on the tins of food, a poster advertising the new method, and advertisements to run in newspapers.

1810–1860: Transportation Revolution

Skills: Research, thinking, writing, map skills.

Objectives: Students learn how advances in transportation facilitated both economic development and the westward movement in the United States during the mid-1800's.

Project: Railroad map.

Suggested Group Roles: Reader, recorder, artist.

Suggested Group Size: Three to four students in each group.

Materials Needed: *Transportation Revolution* handout; notebook paper and pens; research materials to be provided by students; blank paper, markers, colored pencils. Optional: copies of blank outline map of the United States from page 131.

Procedure: Distribute handout and discuss with students. If desired, distribute copies of blank outline map of the United States for student use. Form groups. Set date for students to complete research and begin group work in class. Display completed maps in classroom.

Evaluation: Grade on completeness, accuracy, and neatness.

Variation: Have some groups research railroads, while others research—and illustrate on a map—the development of canals in the same period.

1810–1860: Transportation Revolution

Between 1810 and 1860, a transportation revolution took place in America. A transatlantic ship sailed regularly between New York and Liverpool, England. The crossing took about 30 days. The Cumberland Road, from Cumberland, Maryland, to Vandalia, Illinois, was begun in 1811. It became an important westward route. But the two most important developments were canals and railroads.

Find out what railroad lines were built in the United States between 1810 and 1860. Create a map of the United States to show these railroads. Give your map a caption. Write a paragraph at the bottom of the map, describing the importance of the railroad in the United States during the 1800's.

Here are some questions to get you started:

- Who paid for these railroads? _____

- What areas did they connect? _____

  _____

- What goods were shipped by them? _____

  _____

- Did they also connect with other means of transportation? _____

- Were they successful? _____

1830: Sequoyah and the Talking Leaves

Skills: Comprehension, problem solving, visual skills, writing.

Objectives: Students learn about the development of the first method for writing a Native American language.

Project: Memorial design.

Suggested Group Roles: Recorder, artist.

Suggested Group Size: Two to three students in each group.

Materials Needed: *Sequoyah and the Talking Leaves* handout; blank paper, markers, colored pencils, pens.

Procedure: Distribute handout and discuss with students. Form groups and have students work as directed in the handout. Display completed designs in the classroom.

Evaluation: Class chooses the most appropriate design. Grade on completeness and originality.

Variations:

1. Have students make a model of their memorial design.

2. Have students design a syllabary for English words, instead of the alphabet we use now. They might consider sounds like *ch, th, sh, kn, tw* as sounds that might have their own symbol, instead of combining two letters to indicate the sound.

1830: Sequoyah and the Talking Leaves

Sequoyah, a Cherokee Indian, was born around 1770. Sequoyah was good at languages. He spoke French, Spanish, and English in addition to his native tongue.

Sequoyah saw that white expansion would harm Cherokee culture. He wanted to help preserve his culture.

The Cherokee had no written language. Sequoyah himself had never learned to read or write in any language. He was fascinated by the "talking leaves" of the white settlers—the pieces of paper on which settlers wrote messages. Sequoyah started to develop a Cherokee system of writing.

At first, he tried to develop symbols for each Cherokee word. Then he worked out a way to adapt the English alphabet for the Cherokee language. He developed a syllabary, where each symbol represents a syllable, or combination of sounds. The English alphabet has 26 letters. Sequoyah needed 86 symbols for the sounds of the Cherokee tongue.

The syllabary was probably finished by 1821. In 1828, the first Indian newspaper, the *Cherokee Phoenix*, began publication. It used Sequoyah's syllabary. Other tribes were able to adapt Sequoyah's syllabary to their own languages. Thousands of Native Americans were now able to read and write their native tongues. During the Indian removal, Sequoyah's gift helped a divided people to stay connected.

Sequoyah's contribution to writing is unique. He is the only person in history to have single-handedly devised a way to write a language.

When the Cherokee were removed to Oklahoma, they wanted to name the area Sequoyah, in his honor. The U.S. government would not allow it. However, the magnificent California redwood, the sequoia, is named for him.

Think about Sequoyah and his remarkable achievement. Then design a fitting memorial for him. Underneath your design, explain why you chose the memorial you did.

1843: The Oregon Trail

Skills: Research, problem solving, writing, visual skills.

Objectives: Students investigate the westward movement.

Project: Restaurant plan and menu.

Suggested Group Roles: Reader, recorder, artist.

Suggested Group Size: Two to three students per group.

Materials Needed: _The Oregon Trail_ handout; notebook paper and pens; blank paper, markers, colored pencils; research materials provided by students.

Procedure: Distribute handout and discuss with students. Form groups. If students are already very familiar with the westward movement, group work can begin immediately. Otherwise, set date for students to complete research and begin group work in class. Post completed plans and menus on a bulletin board display.

Evaluation: Students choose the most interesting and successful restaurant plan and menu. Grade plans and menus on completeness and authenticity and (optional) quality of artwork.

Variations:

1. Have some students prepare plans for the restaurant, and have some write newspaper reviews of such a restaurant.

2. Have students prepare some foods that might have been eaten by people on the Oregon Trail, and have an Oregon Trail food sampling in class.

Name _____   Date _____

1843: The Oregon Trail

Disputed by Great Britain and United States

Oregon Territory

Indian Country

Iowa Territory

Wisconsin Territory

OREGON TRAIL

Franklin

Independence

St. Louis

Illinois

Missouri

Arkansas

Red River

(continued)

57   *61 Cooperative Learning Activities in U.S. History*

1843: The Oregon Trail *(continued)*

You have decided to open a new theme restaurant, The Oregon Trail. You plan to have your restaurant celebrate the people who went west over the Oregon Trail. Everything in your restaurant will be an authentic recreation of the Oregon Trail experience—even the food.

Develop a plan and menu for your restaurant, using only foods that might have been eaten by people traveling west to the Oregon Territory from the 1840's on. Your plan should include a written description of the restaurant and its appearance. Include a floor plan to show how the seating would be arranged. If you wish, you can illustrate your plan and menu with appropriate images.

Here are some questions to get you started:

- What foods might people on the Oregon Trail have carried with them? _____

  _____

- What foods might they have found or bought along the way? _____

  _____

- What kind of cooking equipment did they have? _____

  _____

- Would they have been able to bake food? _____

- What could you use for seating, to suggest the seating used along the Oregon Trail?

  _____

- How will you decorate the restaurant? _____

  _____

- How will the wait staff be dressed? _____

1830's–1850's: Lowell Mills

Skills: Comprehension, problem solving, writing, speaking.

Objectives: Students explore the effects of industrialization and how women's roles were changing in the 1800's.

Project: Oral presentation.

Suggested Group Roles: Reader, recorder, checker, speaker.

Suggested Group Size: Two to three students in each group.

Materials Needed: *Lowell Mills* handout; notebook paper and pens.

Procedure: Distribute handout and discuss with students. Form groups and have students work as directed in the handout. One member from each group presents the group's plan to the class. After a class discussion, the most workable plan is chosen.

Evaluation: Grade on clarity, accuracy, and oral presentation.

Variations:

1. Form class into two teams, which debate whether or not the state should step in to change conditions at the Lowell mills.

2. Have students research the layout of factory buildings and dormitories for female workers in the town of Lowell, then make a model of the town or create a poster showing a bird's-eye view of the town.

1830's–1850's: Lowell Mills

Until the 1830's, goods like textiles and shoes were made by artisans. The artisans usually worked in their own homes and made the goods by hand.

Power machinery changed all that. Now all the work could be done on a large scale, in factory buildings. The factory system became common in America.

Mill owners needed cheap, reliable labor. They advertised for women workers. The ads offered good wages and pleasant living conditions.

Many unmarried farm women went to Lowell and other factory towns to work. They soon realized that the ads hadn't told the whole story. The work was hard, and the hours were long.

In 1845, factory workers asked the state for help. They wanted to limit work to 10 hours a day. A committee was set up to look at labor conditions in the mills. Several factory workers told the committee of their experiences. This is part of the record of mill worker Eliza R. Hemmingway's statement:

> Her wages average $16 to $23 a month exclusive of board. She complained of the hours for labor being too many, and the time for meals too limited. In the summer season, the work is commenced at 5 o'clock, A.M., and continued until 7 o'clock, P.M., with half an hour for breakfast and three quarters of an hour for dinner. During 8 months of the year, but half an hour is allowed for dinner. The air in the room she considered not to be wholesome. There were 293 small lamps and 61 large lamps lighted in the room in which she worked, when evening work is required. These lamps are also lighted sometimes in the morning. About 130 females, 11 men, and 12 children (between the ages of 11 and 14) work in the room with her.

The committee listened to statements from factory workers and employers. They visited mills in Lowell to look at the working conditions. The committee decided that conditions at the mills did not need to be changed. They did not recommend a 10-hour day.

Your group formed part of the committee. You were shocked by conditions in the mills. You don't agree that nothing needs to change. Based on Eliza Hemmingway's testimony, and your own knowledge, draw up a plan to improve labor conditions for Lowell factory workers. Identify each problem condition and a solution or solutions for each one. Present your plan to the class.

1845: Baseball Rules

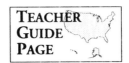

Skills: Comprehension, thinking, speaking.

Objectives: Students consider the development of different aspects of American culture.

Project: Conversation created and acted out.

Suggested Group Roles: Recorder, checker, coordinator, speakers.

Suggested Group Size: Three to four students in each group.

Materials Needed: *Baseball Rules* handout; notebook paper and pens.

Procedure: Distribute handout and discuss with students. Form groups and have students work as directed in the handout. Students act out conversations for the class.

Evaluation: Grade on completeness, originality, and oral presentation.

Variations:

1. Have students write a newspaper account of this early baseball game. Completed accounts can be "published" in a special baseball news sheet.

2. Have students create a radio report of this first baseball game. Encourage them to develop creative sound effects to suggest the sounds of the game and add atmosphere.

1845: Baseball Rules

Until close to the Civil War, Americans played cricket more than baseball. There were cricket teams in New York and Philadelphia, in Detroit and Connecticut. The All-United States team beat the All-Canada team in an international match and considered challenging the English cricket team.

In 1842, a group of young men working on Wall Street were inspired by all these cricket players to try exercising after office hours. But instead of playing cricket, they voted for the field ball game they had played as boys. It was based on an English game called rounders.

The group rented a field in Hoboken, New Jersey, in a picnic grove called the Elysian Fields. The players met twice a week. They built a clubhouse, kept a score book, and fixed a system of fines for nonattendance. In 1845, the Knickerbocker Base Ball Club wrote out rules for a new game it called "baseball." The game caught on.

You and your group live in Hoboken in 1845. You have just watched one of the first baseball games at the Elysian Fields. You have never seen this game played quite like this before. What might be new about it? What features of the game might account for its popularity?

Create and act out a conversation about the game you just saw. Describe it in as much detail as you can.

1849: Dr. Blackwell

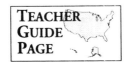

Skills: Thinking, writing, speaking.

Objectives: Students learn about changing gender roles in the United States in the 1800's.

Project: Interview, created and role-played.

Suggested Group Roles: Recorder, coordinator, speakers.

Suggested Group Size: Two students in each group.

Materials Needed: *Dr. Blackwell* handout; notebook paper and pens.

Procedure: Distribute handout and discuss with students. Depending on your class, you may require students to prepare a written script for the dialogue, or you may allow them to role-play extemporaneously. Form groups and have students work as directed in the handout. Pairs of students present dialogues to the class. If a video camera is available, you may wish to videotape the student presentations.

Evaluation: Grade on oral presentation.

1849: Dr. Blackwell

Elizabeth Blackwell was born in England. She came to the United States as a child. As a young woman, she taught in a school. Then, in 1843, she became interested in medicine. When she tried to enter medical school, she was turned down again and again. The schools she applied to only accepted male students.

A total of 29 medical schools rejected her application. She was finally accepted as a student by the Geneva Medical School in New York.

Even then, Blackwell had problems to overcome. The people in the town avoided her. People stared at her as she walked to classes. Some professors didn't want her in their classes. She was asked not to attend some demonstrations and dissections. But she kept her goal in sight. In 1849, Elizabeth Blackwell graduated as an M.D. She was the first woman in the world to earn a medical degree.

Prepare an interview between a journalist and Dr. Blackwell. Consider what questions the interviewer might want to ask and what answers Dr. Blackwell might give. Questions you might want to ask include:

- What first interested you in medicine?

- How did you feel when the established medical schools turned you down?

- What made you keep going?

- How do you feel now that you have done what you set out to do?

- What are your plans for the future?

Present your interview to the class in the form of a dialogue, with one group member playing the part of the interviewer and the other playing Dr. Blackwell.

1850's: Working Children

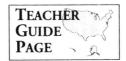

Skills: Research, thinking, writing.

Objectives: Students understand how the factory system affected the lives of individuals.

Project: Written first-person account.

Suggested Group Roles: Reader, recorder.

Suggested Group Size: Two to three students in each group.

Materials Needed: *Working Children* handout; notebook paper and pens; research materials to be provided by students.

Procedure: Distribute handout and discuss with students. Form groups. Set date for students to complete research and begin group work in class. Make a bulletin board display with the completed accounts.

Evaluation: Grade on accuracy, organization, and originality.

Variations:

1. Have some groups create illustrations of work in the different settings named.

2. Have students create a song bewailing the fate of a child factory laborer. If they wish, they can set their lyrics to the music of an existing song.

1850's: Working Children

In the United States today, the law says that everyone under the age of 16 must go to school. If you have a job after school, you can only work a certain number of hours. Some students think this is too strict. They want to be able to buy things, and they need to work to do this.

The laws weren't always so strict. In the early years of this country, children had to work. On the farm they worked in the fields, in the barn, in the house. In cities, they worked in factories or in "sweatshops." In coalfields, they worked in the mines.

In 1842, the state of Massachusetts passed a law limiting child labor. Children under 12 couldn't work more than 10 hours a day. For many families, this law meant a big loss of income. Some children lied about their ages to get jobs.

Find out about the history of child labor. Choose work in a coal mine, a factory, or a city "sweatshop." Then imagine you are a 12-year-old in one of these jobs. Write an account of your typical day.

- What time do you get up?

- What do you have for breakfast?

- How do you get to work?

- What time do you start work?

- What breaks do you have during the day?

- What do you have for lunch?

- How are you treated by your employer?

- What happens if you make a mistake?

- What are your working conditions: wet or dry? warm or cold? Is the air healthy to breathe?

- Do you work standing up, sitting, or crawling?

- When do you finish work?

- What do you eat for supper?

- When do you go to bed?

- What do you see as your future?

1780–1865: Underground Railroad Hall of Fame

Skills: Research, comprehension, thinking, writing, speaking.

Objectives: Students research the extent of the Underground Railroad and the determination of African Americans to remove themselves from slavery.

Project: Oral nominations based on written sheets.

Suggested Group Roles: Reader, recorder, speaker.

Suggested Group Size: Two to four students in each group.

Materials Needed: *Underground Railroad Hall of Fame* handout; notebook paper and pens; research materials to be provided by students.

Procedure: Distribute handout and discuss with students. Form groups. Set date for students to complete research and begin group work in class. Groups present their completed nominations to the class. Then have the class decide who should be included in the Hall of Fame. A few names—Levi Coffin, Thomas Garrett, Frederick Douglass, Harriet Tubman, the Grimké sisters—will appear on many lists. Students may choose to include only those who received multiple votes or to include everyone who is nominated. Create a Freedom Hall of Fame bulletin board with the nomination sheets.

Evaluation: Grade on completeness, accuracy, and oral presentation.

Variation: Have students design a monument to the people who made the Underground Railroad a reality. They can create a drawing of their monument, or a model in paper, clay, papier-mâché, or other suitable materials.

1780–1865: Underground Railroad Hall of Fame

Some Routes of the Underground Railroad

(continued)

1780–1865: Underground Railroad
Hall of Fame *(continued)*

Between 1780 and 1865, 100,000 enslaved African Americans escaped to freedom by the Underground Railroad. As many as 3,000 people acted as "conductors" along the way.

The words "Underground Railroad" suggest something organized. It's easy to imagine escaping slaves just walking up to the "station," buying a "ticket," and heading north to freedom. But the Underground Railroad was never that clearly defined. If it had been, it would have been too easy for slave-hunters to stop.

Instead, the "railroad" was more like a series of networks. Along each network, people tried to help escapees make their way northward. These helpers might be black or white, slave or free, Northern or Southern. They might never have the chance to help more than one fugitive slave. They might be able to help thousands. All of them were part of the Underground Railroad that helped bring former slaves to freedom.

Your group has been asked to set up a Freedom Hall of Fame. Your first job is to nominate workers from the Underground Railroad to be included in the Hall of Fame. You must name at least five people, but you can name as many more as you wish.

For each name, prepare a nomination sheet. The sheet should describe the person's contributions to the Underground Railroad and the reason he or she should be included in the Freedom Hall of Fame. If you wish, illustrate each sheet with a portrait of your nominee or with a scene from the Underground Railroad.

Present your nominations orally to the class.

1850's: Two Faces of Slavery

Skills: Comprehension, thinking, writing.

Objectives: Students examine the rationalizations of proslavery speakers and the realities of what enslavement meant.

Project: Written newspaper story.

Suggested Group Roles: Reader, recorder.

Suggested Group Size: Two students in each group.

Materials needed: *Two Faces of Slavery* handout; notebook paper and pens.

Procedure: Distribute handout and discuss with students. Form groups and have students work as directed in the handout. If you wish, completed articles can be combined and published in a special slavery news sheet.

Evaluation: Grade on completeness and clarity.

Variations:

1. Form students into groups of four. Give students the Lowell Mills handout as well as this one. Two students in each group should take one side of the slavery issue and debate whether or not slaves are better off than paid workers in a factory.

2. Although slaves were kept from learning to write, no laws could keep them from expressing themselves. Many powerful songs about the slave experience were created by slaves. Have students create an antislavery song based on John Jackson's description of his life as a slave. If students wish, they can set their words to the music of an existing song.

1850's: Two Faces of Slavery

People who were in favor of slavery said they were really only helping the people they enslaved. In 1835, the governor of South Carolina described the life of slaves in these words:

> There is not upon the face of the earth any class of people, high or low, so perfectly free from care and anxiety . . . .Our slaves are cheerful, contented, and happy, [unlike] the general condition of the human race.

John Jackson, a former slave, described his life this way:

> My younger days were happy ones. I played with the massa's children until I became seven or eight years old, then I had to go into the field with the other black folks and work hard all day from earliest dawn till late at night. We ate twice a day, that is, when we got up in the morning we were driven out into the fields and were called into breakfast at noon by the blast of an old tin horn.

> All we got to eat then was three corn cake dumplins and one plate of soup. No meat unless there happened to be a rotten piece in the smoke house. This would be given to us to make our soup. Why the dogs got better eating than we poor colored folks. We would go out into the fields again and work very hard until dark, when we were driven in by the crack of the overseer's lash and frequently that crack meant blood from some unfortunate creature's back, who, becoming weary, had shown signs of faltering.

Use these two excerpts to write a newspaper article on slavery. Include the pro-slavery arguments. Then use material from John Jackson's narrative to challenge them.

1800–1860: People of the Plains

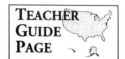

Skills: Research, thinking, writing, map skills.

Objectives: Students learn about the diversity of Native American societies, even when referred to under a group name by European Americans.

Project: Comparative chart with optional map.

Suggested Group Roles: Reader, recorder, coordinator, artist.

Suggested Group Size: Four to five students in each group.

Materials Needed: *People of the Plains* handout; notebook paper and pens; research material to be provided by students; blank paper, markers, colored pencils.

Procedure: Distribute handout and discuss with students. Form groups. Set date for students to complete research and begin group work in class as directed in the handout. Display completed charts and maps in the classroom.

Evaluation: Grade charts on completeness, accuracy, and presentation.

Variation: Assign one Native American tribe to each group of students to research. They can combine their research into a written report, a visual display, or a model showing the way of life of the particular people they examined.

1800–1860: People of the Plains

When people speak of Native American cultures, they often use group names to refer to a number of different tribes, such as Woodlands Indians, Southwest Indians, or Plains Indians. The tribes in these groupings usually have some things in common. Still, it would be a mistake to think that all tribes included in a grouping had the same culture.

The peoples called "Plains Indians" originally came from different areas. They spoke many different languages and had various customs. The Plains Indians include the Ojibway, Blood, Blackfoot, Gros Ventre, Cree, Assiniboin, Hidatsa, Mandan, Arikara, Dakota, Arapaho, Cheyenne, Pawnee, Iowa, Oto, Kansa, Kiowa, Crow, Jicarilla Apache, Mescalero Apache, Comanche, Lipan Apache, Kiowa Apache, Wichita, and Osage peoples.

Find out about the ways of life of at least three of these Plains peoples. Make a chart to show their differences and similarities.

Here are some questions you may want to ask:

- What language did this people speak?

- What was their system of religious beliefs?

- Was descent reckoned through the father, through the mother, or through both?

- Where on the Great Plains did they live?

- What kind of houses did they build?

- What did they hunt?

- What weapons did they use in hunting?

- Did they grow any of their own food? What did they grow, and how?

- How did they dress?

If you wish, you can include a map with your chart. It could show the areas occupied by the tribes you investigated.

1861–1865: Message in Code

Skills: Comprehension, problem solving, thinking, writing.

Objectives: Students see how the resources—and resourcefulness—of the Union and the Confederacy affected the course of the Civil War.

Project: Coded message.

Suggested Group Roles: Recorder, checker, evaluator.

Suggested Group Size: Two to four students in each group.

Materials Needed: *Message in Code* handout; access to reference material on codes and ciphers, such as encyclopedias; notebook paper and pens.

Procedure: Distribute handout and discuss with students. Form groups and have students work as directed in the handout. Groups exchange their coded messages and keys, and decipher each other's messages. Display the messages and keys in the classroom.

Evaluation: Students decide which code was the most successful.

Variations:

1. Have student groups exchange messages, but keep the code secret. See if groups can crack each other's codes.

2. Using the larger group size, have students create a math-based code for their message. One or two students in each group can work on creating the message, while the others work on creating the code.

1861–1865: Message in Code

As soon as the Civil War began, President Lincoln imposed a blockade on Southern ports. He had U.S. ships stationed outside those ports to stop any ships from going in or out. This meant that the Confederacy could not export things like cotton to get money. It also couldn't import military equipment and food. And the blockade made it a lot more difficult for Southerners to get messages to each other.

You're a Southerner, trying to get a message out past the North's blockade of Southern ports. You don't want the enemy to read your message if it falls into their hands. What can you do?

You might try sending your message in code. Both North and South used codes to keep their messages secret. The Union Army used "transposition ciphers." A key word showed which order to read the columns in. The Confederate Army often used a code where one letter of the alphabet was always substituted for another. The Union forces were able to solve most of the Confederate codes. But since the Union codes were more complex, the Confederacy often couldn't solve them. Confederate officials sometimes even published Union coded messages in newspapers, asking readers to help solve the code and read the message!

Some codes are very simple, and some are very complex. The substitution systems are the simplest. Here are some examples:

1. Relate each letter to a number: A=1, B=2, C=3, etc. The word CODE would become 3 15 4 5.

2. Substitute one letter for another: A=R, B=F, C=N, D=P, E=F, O=Z. The word CODE would become NZPF.

Choose one of the methods described here, or do research to find out about other codes. Use your code to write a message about the situation in the South. How is morale among the soldiers? among the citizens? How are supplies holding out? Is there any news about troop movements? Put the message in code. Write the key on a separate piece of paper. Then exchange messages with another group and try to decipher their message.

1860's: War Report

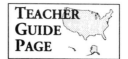

Skills: Research, writing, visual skills.

Objectives: Students explore the effects of the war on society in general, as presented to them by journalists.

Project: Illustrated newspaper article.

Suggested Group Roles: Reader, recorder.

Suggested Group Size: Two students in each group.

Materials Needed: *War Report* handout; notebook paper and pens; research materials to be provided by students.

Procedure: Distribute handout and discuss with students. Form groups. Set date for students to complete research and begin group work in class. Create a bulletin board display of finished articles.

Evaluation: Grade on accuracy, clarity, organization, and effectiveness of illustrations.

Variations:

1. Have students produce a special report on the Civil War. Either let students choose their own topics, or assign specific events to each group. Tell students to include at least one illustration with their article. After all articles have been completed, look at the design of actual newspapers to create a newspaper banner, masthead, etc. If you have access to a desktop publishing system, use it to create your newspaper. Otherwise, use a computer to print articles in narrow columns, or have students hand-print the articles to look like newspaper columns. Display the completed newspaper in the classroom.

2. Have students discuss the pros and cons of putting journalists and photographers at risk on the battlefield. Form groups of four students. Two of them should play the role of newspaper editors, while the other two should be journalists and photographers. Students present their best arguments to the class.

3. The telegraph changed the way news was gathered and how it was delivered. The development of radio and television changed the news again, giving events far more immediacy as people came to hear and see what happened. Have students imagine how the Civil War would have been presented if broadcast media had been invented in the 1860's. Then have them prepare a contemporaneous radio or TV news presentation on the event they have researched.

Name _____ Date _____

1860's: War Report

Before the telegraph, the "news" in American newspapers was often quite old. Journalists had to depend on slow methods of transportation. They often had to wait a long time to hear about important events or to report on them.

By the 1850's, the telegraph and the railroad reached as far west as Chicago. Newspapers could report on events while they were still recent. Many newspapers took sides on the slavery debate. They helped publicize the controversy between North and South.

The Civil War was the first American war to receive a lot of newspaper coverage. It was also the first to be recorded in photographs. However, the photographs could not be directly reproduced in newspapers. The images in the photographs were carefully carved on wooden blocks. The blocks were then used to print the newspaper images.

Some journalists became important people. The press could make or break the career of army officers.

Your group is a team of journalists. You are in the field to report on the Civil War. Prepare a newspaper article on an incident in the war that you think is important. Research the incident to find out all about it. Include as much information as you can in your article. Add sketches or descriptions of the photographs that should accompany the article. You must include at least one illustration for your article.

1865–1873: Symbols and the Gilded Age

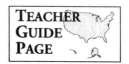

Skills: Research, problem solving, writing, visual skills.

Objectives: Students research the rampant materialism that defined this period.

Project: Illustration of symbol.

Suggested Group Roles: Recorder, artist.

Suggested Group Size: Two students in each group.

Materials Needed: *Symbols and the Gilded Age* handout; blank paper, markers, colored pencils.

Procedure: Distribute handout and discuss with students. Form groups. Set date for students to complete research and begin group work in class as directed in the handout. Display completed symbols in the classroom.

Evaluation: Grade symbols on appropriateness, neatness, and originality.

1865–1873: Symbols and the Gilded Age

The period from 1865 to 1873 is sometimes called "The Gilded Age." This phrase comes from the title of a novel by Mark Twain and Charles Dudley Warner. In the novel, the writers showed the corruption of the period. Many people seemed only to think about getting rich. The authors used the phrase "The Gilded Age" to symbolize what they saw as wrong with this period. They meant that everything looked nice and shiny on the outside, but it wasn't really gold. It was just a gold-colored coating on a shoddy interior.

A symbol is defined as "an object used to stand for something abstract." The "something abstract" can be anything—an idea, a belief, a period of time. We use a dove or an olive branch to symbolize the idea of peace. We use the cross to symbolize the belief of Christianity. We could use the peace sign to symbolize the decade of the sixties, or the "V for victory" sign to symbolize the Allies in World War II.

Think of the different symbols you see around you every day. Think of how the symbol comes to represent the idea behind it. Then come up with something that you think symbolizes the Gilded Age in American history, from 1865 to 1873. You will probably need to read more about the Gilded Age first.

Here are some questions to help you get started:

• What do you see as the most important events of this period? _____

_____

• The most important people? _____

_____

• The most important attitudes? _____

_____

Draw a picture of your symbol. Write a few sentences explaining why you chose this as a symbol.

1865–1880: Reconstruction

Skills: Research, problem solving, comprehension, visual skills.

Objectives: Students understand the various Reconstruction programs proposed for the South.

Project: Comparative chart.

Suggested Group Roles: Reader, recorder, coordinator, checker.

Suggested Group Size: Four students in each group.

Materials Needed: *Reconstruction* handout; notebook paper and pens; blank paper, markers, colored pencils; research materials to be provided by students.

Procedure: Distribute handout and discuss with students. Form groups. If your U.S. history text offers a good description of the various Reconstruction plans, direct students to read the relevant section. Otherwise, set date for students to complete research and begin group work in class as directed in the handout. Display completed charts in the classroom.

Evaluation: Did students include all the Reconstruction plans named on the handout? Does the chart show their differences and similarities? Does the chart show the South's reaction to each plan? Did students include a summary paragraph? Is the chart neatly executed? Does it have a title?

1865–1880: Reconstruction

The Civil War ended with the surrender of the South. The North had won. Slavery was over—by law. But it's often easier to say, "It's over" than actually to end something.

After the Civil War, different people suggested different ways to rebuild the country while making sure that slavery was really ended. Lincoln had a plan for Reconstruction before he died. In fact, his last public address, four days before his death, was about Reconstruction. In 1864, Congress passed a Reconstruction plan called the Wade-Davis Reconstruction Bill. President Lincoln vetoed it. When Andrew Johnson became president, he formed his own plan. The Reconstruction Acts of 1866–1868 took yet another approach.

Find out as much as you can about all these plans for Reconstruction. Compare them. What did they demand from the Southern states? What did they promise the South? Did they make sure African Americans could use their rights as citizens? Did the Southern states accept the conditions, or did they try to find a way around them?

Make a chart to show Reconstruction in the South. Include the different plans listed above. Show what each one promised and required. Describe the South's reaction to each plan. Your chart should show how the plans were similar and how they were different.

Give your chart a title. At the bottom of your chart, write a brief paragraph explaining how well the aims of Reconstruction had been met by 1880.

1868: Johnson's Impeachment

Skills: Research, comprehension, writing, speaking.

Objectives: Students investigate the extent of the political controversy over Reconstruction.

Project: Presentation of original play.

Suggested Group Roles: Reader, recorder, coordinator, checker.

Suggested Group Size: Four to five students in each group.

Materials Needed: *Johnson's Impeachment* handout; notebook paper and pens; research material and props or other items for the play to be provided by students.

Procedure: Distribute handout and discuss with students. Form groups. Set date for students to complete research and begin group work in class as directed in the handout. Students act out their plays for the class.

Evaluation: Grade written scenes and oral presentation.

Variations:

1. Assign a different scene to each group. Then have groups present their scenes in order to play out the whole drama.

2. Have students develop and perform a mock trial of President Johnson. One group should represent Johnson and his advisers, one group Ross and his supporters. A third group should represent the Radical Republicans, and a fourth Johnson's supporters in the Senate. A fifth group could represent and support Thaddeus Stevens, whose desire for Johnson's impeachment was so strong that, ill as he was, he had himself carried into the chamber to hear the result of the vote.

1868: Johnson's Impeachment

We often think that being a hero means not being afraid of danger. When we think of heroes of the Civil War period, we think of people who risked their lives for a cause.

The Reconstruction Era has a different kind of hero. He isn't known for facing enemy guns. He is a hero because he refused to agree with his colleagues.

After the Civil War, President Johnson had trouble with Congress. The Radical Republicans disagreed with him about how the South should be treated. Tension between the president and Congress grew. Finally, the Radical Republicans felt they had to get rid of the president. In 1868, they accused Johnson of doing illegal things while in office. If he was found guilty, he would be removed from office.

The president was tried before the Senate. The trial lasted about two months. To remove the president from office, two thirds of the senators would have to find him guilty. It was obvious that Johnson was not guilty of crimes against the state. Still, many senators voted to remove him from office.

There were 54 senators. Of these, 35 had already said they would vote against Johnson. Another 18 said they would vote in his favor. One more vote against Johnson would put him out of office.

The only senator who had not yet made up his mind was Edmund G. Ross of Kansas. The Radical Republicans pressured him to vote for conviction. He was told he would never hold office again if he voted the wrong way. He got death threats in the mail. After the trial, Ross said:

> I almost literally looked down into my open grave. Friendships, position, fortune, everything that makes life desirable to an ambitious man were about to be swept away by the breath of my own mouth, perhaps forever.

Ross voted for acquittal. He was never elected to the Senate again.

Create a play showing the most dramatic moments in Johnson's impeachment trial. Include the Radical Republicans trying to convince Ross to vote for conviction and the final vote in the Senate. Act out your play for the class.

1860–1890: The Last of the West

Skills: Research, thinking, writing, visual skills.

Objectives: Students learn about key cultural factors in western life during the second half of the nineteenth century.

Project: Written report.

Suggested Group Roles: Reader, recorder, artist, evaluator.

Suggested Group Size: Two to four students in each group.

Materials Needed: *The Last of the West* handout; notebook paper and pens; research materials to be provided by students; blank paper, markers, colored pencils.

Procedure: Distribute handout and discuss with students. Form groups. Set date for students to complete research and begin group work in class as directed in the handout. Display completed reports on a "Last of the West" bulletin board.

Evaluation: Grade on completeness, accuracy, and originality.

Variations:

1. Have some groups research the West of mining towns while others investigate the West of cattle ranches, of hunters and trappers, and of homesteading farmers on the Great Plains.

2. Have students prepare an outline for a realistic movie about the last of the West. The outline should include a synopsis of the plot, a list of characters, and sketches showing sets and costumes.

1860–1890: The Last of the West

Moviemakers have always been fascinated by the American West. How many Westerns have you seen? How realistic or accurate do you think they were? Especially during the 1950's and 1960's, the picture of the West seen in movies was a very unrealistic one.

A new movie is being made about the last frontiers of the West. The movie is to be set in a mining town. You have been hired as a consultant. Your job is to provide information about the period and the way of life of the time.

Read as much as you can about mining towns in the West. Write a report about them for the movie production company. Include advice and information on food, clothing, weapons, tools, environment, and customs in general. If possible, include drawings and photographs to illustrate your material.

Use this space to start your notes.

Food _____

_____

Clothing _____

_____

Weapons _____

_____

Tools _____

_____

Environment _____

_____

Customs _____

_____

1890: American Frontiers

Skills: Research, map skills.

Objectives: Students see the cyclical pattern of United States territorial expansion.

Project: Frontier map.

Suggested Group Roles: Recorder, artist, checker.

Suggested Group Size: Two to three students in each group.

Materials Needed: *American Frontiers* handout; notebook paper and pens; blank paper, markers, colored pencils. Optional: copies of blank outline map of United States on page 131.

Procedure: Distribute handout and discuss with students. If you wish, pass out copies of the blank outline map of the United States on page 131. Assign a different date in history to each group; the group will then research, and create a map for, the frontier at that date. Appropriate dates would include:

> 1700—British settlements along the coast from Maine to South Carolina
> 1763—Proclamation of 1763 restricts settlement to lands east of the Appalachian Mountains
> 1785—The original 13 colonies and territory acquired from Great Britain
> 1803—The Louisiana Purchase
> 1819—The Adams-Onis Treaty completes accession of Florida
> 1845—Annexation of Texas
> 1846—Oregon Country dispute with Great Britain is settled
> 1848—Mexican cession
> 1853—The Gadsden Purchase
> 1867—The Alaska Purchase

Set date for students to complete research and begin group work in class. Display completed maps in the classroom.

Evaluation: Grade on completeness, accuracy, and neatness. Does the map include a key and a title?

Variation: Have student groups role-play a family debating whether or not to head for the frontier in a given period. Be sure students include both advantages and disadvantages of such a move.

1890: American Frontiers

A frontier is an area where settled land gives way to wilderness. By 1890, although there were still wilderness areas in the United States, there were no long stretches of continuous land that had not been settled. The federal government announced that the United States no longer had a frontier.

In the history of the United States, there have been many frontiers. The first settlement at Jamestown, Virginia, established the first frontier. As settlers took over an area, they began to edge west. When this movement hit a natural barrier—like a mountain range—the movement slowed. When the population east of the barrier became dense enough, the westward movement began again. A new frontier was formed.

Create a map of the United States to show where the frontier was at a certain date. Use color and shading to show the frontier. Don't forget to include a key explaining your map and a title describing what it shows.

Susan B. Anthony Opera

Skills: Research, thinking, problem solving, writing, visual skills.

Objectives: Students learn about the beginnings of the organized women's movement in the United States.

Project: Written outline of an opera act.

Suggested Group Roles: Reader, coordinator, recorder.

Suggested Group Size: Three to four students in each group; whole class.

Materials Needed: *Susan B. Anthony Opera* handout; notebook paper and pens; research materials to be provided by students; blank paper and pencils.

Procedure: Distribute handout and discuss with students. As a class, discuss the Susan B. Anthony opera students will create. Decide on the scope of the opera and what should happen in each act. These are some of the questions that students should decide on in advance:

- What kind of music will your opera use?

- What events do you wish to include in your opera?

- What is the time span of your opera?

- Who are the characters in the opera?

- Where and when does each scene takes place?

- What will the opera be called?

Then assign one act to each group. Each group writes an outline of the scenes in its act and provides sketches of set designs. Display completed outlines in the classroom, or have groups read their outlines in order, from Act 1 to the end of the opera.

Evaluation: Grade on completeness and originality.

Susan B. Anthony Opera

Opera is a form of theater. It combines the dialogue of a play with music. Usually, the performers sing their lines instead of speaking them. Opera music is often classical, but operas have also used jazz, folk, rock, and pop music.

In 1947, a composer named Virgil Thompson wrote an opera. He called it *The Mother of Us All*. The text (known as the libretto, or "little book") was written by Gertrude Stein. The subject was Susan B. Anthony. Thompson set Stein's words to very singable music, based on the folk song tradition. The opera holds a unique place in American music.

How would you go about preparing the script for an opera about Susan B. Anthony? Would you focus on a few of the dramatic events in her life? Or would you show how long she spent working for women's rights? When would your opera begin? When would it end?

Your class is going to prepare a written outline for an opera about Susan B. Anthony. Your group will prepare the outline for one act. The outline for your act should include the names of all the characters and a brief description of each scene. You should also include a sketch for the set design—that is, the way the stage should look during a scene.

Do any of the performers in a scene have particularly important messages to convey? If so, you might wish to give that performer a solo, so that the audience will focus on the words of that song. (A song performed by one singer is called a solo. When two performers sing together, it is a duet. Three singers form a trio, four a quartet. A chorus is a larger group of singers in which more than one person sings each part.)

1871–1930: Mother Jones

Skills: Problem solving, writing.

Objectives: Students learn about the rise of the American labor movement.

Project: Commemorative song.

Suggested Group Roles: Recorder, speaker.

Suggested Group Size: Two to three students in each group.

Materials Needed: *Mother Jones* handout; notebook paper and pens.

Procedure: Distribute handout and discuss with students. Form groups and have students work as directed in the handout. Students sing or recite their songs to the class.

Evaluation: Class chooses the most effective song. Grade all songs on completeness and creativity.

1871–1930: Mother Jones

Mary Harris Jones— "Mother Jones"—was born in Ireland. She moved to Chicago with her family as a girl. She married an ironworker, but her husband died in an epidemic. In 1871, she lost everything she owned in the great Chicago fire and was helped by a labor organization.

She soon became active in the labor movement herself. Mary Jones followed the trail of strikes and labor conflict across the country. Because she called the workers her children, she was given the affectionate title of "Mother."

She was good at getting publicity and attention for workers' causes. Because of this, she became a well-known figure in the labor movement.

Mother Jones organized for the United Mine Workers and supported strikes. She increased public support with her slogan, "Join the union, boys." Mother Jones was also active in trying to stop child labor.

When she died in 1930, many people mourned. She was missed for her fearlessness and dedication.

Write a song in mourning for the death of Mother Jones, and in celebration of her life. You should include the fact that she was most active on behalf of miners and that they viewed her with admiration and affection. If you wish, you can set your words to an existing piece of music. Sing or recite your song to the class (one group member, several, or all).

1877: The Molly Maguires

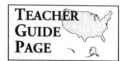

Skills: Comprehension, thinking, writing.

Objectives: Students investigate the conflicts between industrialists and laborers.

Project: Written newspaper account.

Suggested Group Roles: Reader, recorder.

Suggested Group Size: Two students to each group.

Materials Needed: *The Molly Maguires* handout; notebook paper and pens.

Procedure: Distribute handout and discuss with students. Form groups and have students work as directed in the handout. If you wish, you can compile the completed reports into a special Molly Maguire news sheet.

Evaluation: Grade on completeness and originality.

Variations:

1. Divide class into two or three groups. Each group should prepare and act out a mock Molly Maguire trial.

2. The labor movement has always been accompanied by protest songs. Have groups write lyrics for such a song. The song should either protest the mine owners' treatment of laborers or lament the executions of the condemned Mollies. If students wish, they can set their lyrics to the music of an existing song.

1877: The Molly Maguires

Between 1865 and 1876, a group called the Molly Maguires was active in Pennsylvania. At that time, all law enforcement for mining towns was in the hands of the mine owners. Some miners felt that they had to use strong-arm techniques against the owners. Otherwise, they could never improve their bad working conditions. So these miners formed a secret society called the Molly Maguires to achieve their aims.

Soon, mine owners reported a Molly Maguire "crime wave." They said that the Mollies threatened bosses the Mollies identified as unfair. Mine owners said the Mollies even killed some bosses.

In 1875, a Pinkerton detective worked his way undercover into the Molly Maguires. He collected evidence of their actions. Largely on this evidence, 24 coal miners were charged with Molly Maguire crimes. Ten of them were eventually hanged. Much of the evidence used against the miners would not be allowed by a court of law today.

The Mollies were not really a labor organization. Still, people saw them as part of the growing labor movement. The Molly Maguires became a popular legend, especially for people on the workers' side.

You are a reporter in Pennsylvania, reporting on the Molly Maguire trial. Write a newspaper account of the trial.

1800's: Immigrants and Their Contributions

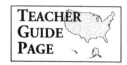

Skills: Research, thinking, map skills.

Objectives: Students explore how immigrants from other countries affected American life.

Project: Map with lists.

Suggested Group Roles: Reader, recorder, artist.

Suggested Group Size: Three to four students in each group.

Materials Needed: *Immigrants and Their Contributions* handout; notebook paper and pens; research materials to be provided by students; blank paper, markers, colored pencils.

Procedure: Distribute handout and discuss with students. Form groups. Set date for students to complete research and begin group work in class as directed in the handout. Display completed maps in the classroom. You may wish to ask students why they think so few immigrant women's names appear on this list, although women also came to this country in large numbers.

Teacher Background: Felix Adler—Germany, social welfare leader, established first free kindergarten in NYC. Louis Agassiz—Switzerland, geologist and zoologist, developed and popularized the idea of an ice age. Alexander Graham Bell—Scotland, invented telephone. Emile Berliner—Germany, contributed to telephone technology, developed phonograph record; Ah Bing—China, developed Bing cherry. Elizabeth Blackwell—England, first woman doctor. Abraham Cahan—Russia, journalist, leader of Socialist party. Andrew Carnegie—Scotland, industrialist, philanthropist, led expansion of U.S. steel industry. Amadeo Giannini—Italy, founded Bank of America. Meyer Guggenheim—Switzerland, industrialist, trustbuster, philanthropist. Mary "Mother Jones" Harris—Ireland, labor organizer. James McCosh—Scotland, philosopher, president of College of New Jersey (now Princeton University). William Mayo—England, doctor, founded hospital now known as Mayo Clinic. Ottmar Mergenthaler—Germany,

(continued)

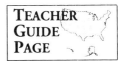

invented Linotype machine for printing. Joseph Pulitzer—Hungary, powerful newspaper publisher. Jacob Riis—Denmark, social reformer. John Roebling—Germany, engineer, suspension bridge builder, including the Brooklyn Bridge. Anna Howard Shaw—England, leader of women's suffrage movement in the United States. Charles P. Steinmetz—Germany, electrical engineer, ideas on alternating current transformed electrical science. Nikola Tesla—Croatia, inventor, discovered the rotating magnetic field, basis of most AC machinery. Charles Van Depoele—Belgium, invented electric railway. Edward Weston—England, electrical engineer, industrialist. Anzia Yezierska—Russia, novelist. Florian Znaniecki—Poland, sociologist, helped make sociology distinct academic discipline. V. K. Zworykin—Russia, inventor, father of modern television.

Evaluation: Grade on completeness and accuracy.

Variation: To make sure that all groups don't pick the same few names, you may wish to assign names to each group. Remember that some individuals may be harder to find information on than others.

1800's: Immigrants and Their Contributions

Since this country was founded, immigrants—people who move here from other countries—have been important. But when immigrants came in large numbers from any one area, U.S. citizens tended to be wary. They pushed to control immigration.

During most of the 1800's, immigration to America was controlled in various ways. For example, newcomers from Asia were largely kept out. So most immigrants during these years came from Europe.

Each of the people listed below came to the United States from somewhere else during the 1800's. Each made an important contribution to American life.

Felix Adler	Meyer Guggenheim	Charles P. Steinmetz
Louis Agassiz	Mary "Mother Jones" Harris	Nikola Tesla
Alexander Graham Bell	James McCosh	Charles Van Depoele
Emile Berliner	William Mayo	Edward Weston
Ah Bing	Ottmar Mergenthaler	Anzia Yezierska
Elizabeth Blackwell	Joseph Pulitzer	Florian Znaniecki
Abraham Cahan	Jacob Riis	V. K. Zworykin
Andrew Carnegie	John Roebling	
Amadeo Giannini	Anna Howard Shaw	

Choose at least five of these immigrants. Prepare a map showing where each one originally came from. List each person's main achievements and contributions.

     61 Cooperative Learning Activities in U.S. History

1891–1895: Queen Liliuokalani

Skills: Comprehension, writing.

Objectives: Students understand some of the political and cultural effects of American expansionism.

Project: Songwriting.

Suggested Group Roles: Recorder, speaker/singer.

Suggested Group Size: Two to three students in each group.

Materials Needed: *Queen Liliuokalani* handout; notebook paper and pens.

Procedure: Distribute handout and discuss with students. Form groups and have students work as directed in the handout. Groups sing or recite their songs to the class.

Evaluation: Students choose the best song. Grade all songs on appropriateness and originality.

Variations:

1. Have students find out more about the revolution of 1893 and write a song about it.

2. In 1898, the same year Queen Liliuokalani wrote "Aloha Oe," she wrote her memoirs, *Hawaii's Story by Hawaii's Queen*. Have students write an entry for the memoirs about either the revolution of 1893 or the insurrection of 1895 and Liliuokalani's abdication.

1891–1895: Queen Liliuokalani

Liliuokalani was the last queen of Hawaii. She was a strong-minded woman and very proud of her Hawaiian culture. She is also known as the author of many songs, including the popular "Aloha Oe."

During the late 1800's, about 5 percent of the people in Hawaii were American. Many of them were sugar growers. Until the early 1890's, sugar could be imported into the United States from Hawaii without paying any duty. Many sugar growers became wealthy.

Then the law was changed. Duty had to be paid on all imported sugar. Hawaiian sugar exports went down. American planters in Hawaii lost money.

Liliuokalani became queen of the Hawaiian Islands in 1891. She started to try to reduce American influence in the islands and restore the islanders' own rule. The American planters felt that the United States and Americans should have more influence in Hawaii, not less. Then they wouldn't have to pay duty on their sugar exports.

John L. Stevens, an American diplomat, helped the planters. Led by Stanford Dole, the planters started a "revolution" against the queen in 1893. Most of the revolutionaries were Americans who had been born in the Islands, or who had lived there for a long time.

To avoid bloodshed, Queen Liliuokalani stepped down from the throne. The planters set up a provisional government.

Queen Liliuokalani appealed to the president of the United States, Grover Cleveland. The United States ordered the provisional government to restore the queen. Dole refused to obey. He said Cleveland had no authority to interfere.

In 1895, there was an uprising in Queen Liliuokalani's name. After it failed, Queen Liliuokalani gave up her royal claims. There was nothing else she could do.

Write a song for Queen Liliuokalani about the loss of her throne. If you wish, you can set your words to the music of an existing song. Sing or recite your song to the class.

1880–1910: The Muckrakers

Skills: Research, comprehension, thinking.

Objectives: Students examine how Americans addressed social roles and economic problems in the late 1800's.

Project: Informational chart.

Suggested Group Roles: Reader, recorder, coordinator, checker.

Suggested Group Size: Three to five students in each group.

Materials Needed: *The Muckrakers* handout; notebook paper and pens; research materials to be provided by students; blank paper and markers.

Procedure: Distribute handout and discuss with students. Form groups. Set date for students to complete research and begin group work in class as directed in the handout. Display completed charts in the classroom. When all work is completed, discuss the role of people like the muckrakers in keeping society safe.

Teacher Background: Student charts should include many of the following people. Samuel Hopkins Adams, *The Great American Fraud*—public health and medicine. Ray Stannard Baker, *The Reign of Lawlessness*—railroad and financial abuses. Stephen Crane, *Maggie: A Girl of the Streets*—slum life. Henry George, *Progress and Poverty*—poverty and capitalism. Thomas Lawson, "Frenzied Finance," article in *Everybody's*—stock market abuses, insurance practices; influenced insurance investigation of 1905. Henry Demarest Lloyd, "The Story of a Great Monopoly," article in *Atlantic Monthly*—the Standard Oil Company. Frank Norris, *The Octopus, The Pit*—the problems of western farmers, including unscrupulous railroad men and shady stock market practices. David Graham Phillips, *Susan Lenox: Her Rise and Fall*—slum life and political corruption; *The Treason of the Senate*—political corruption. Jacob Riis, *How the Other Half Live*—slum life. Charles Edward Russell, *Lawless Wealth*—social dislocation. Upton Sinclair, *The Jungle*—the meat-packing industry. John Spargo, *The Bitter Cry of the Children*—child labor laws. Lincoln Steffens, *The Shame of Cities, The Struggle for Self-Government, The Upbuilders*—political corruption, the alliance between business and politics. Ida M. Tarbell, *History of the Standard Oil Company*—analysis of ruthless business ethics, often condoned by politicians; *The Railroads on Trial*. William Allen White, *Stratagems and Spoils, A Certain Rich Man, In the Heart of a Fool*—corruption in politics.

Evaluation: Grade on completeness, organization, and neatness.

1880–1910: The Muckrakers

In 1906, President Theodore Roosevelt was giving a speech. He referred to some journalists who were exposing corruption. Because of their methods, he called them "muckrakers." He meant that these writers were too busy with dirt and filth to see the fine things in the world.

The term was meant as an insult, but it soon came to be a title of distinction. Muckrakers made people aware of things that went on behind closed doors, in businesses and in politics. Part of the success of the Progressive movement is due to the muckrakers.

Investigate the muckrakers. Find out about as many of them as you can.

Here are some questions to get you started:

- Who were the muckrakers?

- What did they write about?

- Are some of the problems they exposed still here today?

- How could those problems be fixed by people at the time?

Make a chart to show your information. You must include at least five different writers. In one column, give the names of muckraking writers. In a second column, describe a problem that person wrote about. In a third column, suggest some way of fixing the problem. In a fourth column, describe any changes caused by the written piece.

1921: FDR and Handicapped Accessibility

Skills: Research, thinking, writing, speaking.

Objectives: Students explore society's attitude toward physical handicaps in the early twentieth century.

Project: Dialogue, written and then performed.

Suggested Group Roles: Reader, recorder, speakers.

Suggested Group Size: Two students in each group.

Materials Needed: *FDR and Handicapped Access* handout; notebook paper and pens; research materials to be provided by students.

Procedure: Distribute handout and discuss with students. Form groups. Set date for students to complete research and begin group work in class as directed in the handout. Students act out their dialogues to the class. After work is completed, discuss with students the Americans with Disabilities Act of 1990 and how people's attitudes toward physical handicaps have changed since 1932.

Evaluation: Grade on oral presentation.

Variation: Have students act out a scene where Roosevelt's advisers discuss his future with him. His wealthy mother expected him to retire to her home, Hyde Park, and give up his political aspirations. While Eleanor Roosevelt doubted that her husband could ever return to public office, she encouraged him to hope and plan, knowing that having something to aim for would help his health. Louis Howe, Roosevelt's longtime political adviser, also supported him in the idea of remaining active in politics.

1921: FDR and Handicapped Accessibility

In August 1921, Franklin Roosevelt was on vacation with his family. He had been swimming and boating all day and was very tired. He went to bed feeling a little feverish. The next morning, when he woke up, he couldn't move half his body. He had polio and was paralyzed from the hips down.

Before his illness, Roosevelt had been active in politics. He had served in the New York State Senate. He had been assistant secretary of the Navy. Now he wanted to continue his political career. But in the early 1900's, people with physical disabilities were treated as if they were helpless. They were expected to stay home and keep out of sight. Some people thought it was "bad manners" for a "cripple" to go out in public. So how could a man who had lost the use of his legs try to get elected to public office?

Despite the challenges, Franklin Roosevelt was elected to office. In 1929, he became governor of New York. In 1932, he was elected president of the United States.

Find out as much as you can about how President Roosevelt dealt with his disability, and how other people saw him. Write a dialogue between two voters during the 1932 election. Include the answers to as many of these questions as you can in the dialogue:

- What were people's attitudes at the time about disabled people?

- How obvious was Roosevelt's disability?

- How did the press refer to the disability? How did Roosevelt's political opponents refer to it?

- How easy was it for a person in a wheelchair to get around at that period?

- Did any laws require access for handicapped people?

- Were most buildings wheelchair-accessible?

Perform your dialogue for the class.

1925: The Scopes "Monkey" Trial

Skills: Comprehension, thinking, writing.

Objectives: Students learn about how conservative and liberal ideologies clashed in the 1920's.

Project: Written newspaper article.

Suggested Group Roles: Reader, recorder.

Suggested Group Size: Two students in each group.

Materials Needed: *The Scopes "Monkey" Trial* handout; notebook paper and pens.

Procedure: Distribute handout and discuss with students. Form groups and have students work as directed in the handout. Prepare a "monkey trial" bulletin board display with the completed articles.

Evaluation: Grade on completeness and originality.

Variation: Divide the class into two or three groups. Have each group write a scene from the Scopes trial. Characters should include Scopes, Mencken, Bryan, Darrow, the judge, and the jury. Then have groups perform their scenes for classmates.

1925: The Scopes "Monkey" Trial

In March 1925, the state of Tennessee passed a law that made teaching the theory of evolution in school illegal. A biology teacher named John T. Scopes volunteered to test the law, to see if the state could enforce it. In July 1925, Scopes was arrested. His crime: teaching Darwin's theory of evolution.

Scopes's trial was called the "monkey" trial, because the theory of evolution said humans and monkeys came from a common ancestor. The trial attracted a lot of attention. It was seen as a fight between tradition and progress. The prosecutor was William Jennings Bryan, a former presidential candidate. Clarence Darrow, a famous criminal lawyer, defended Scopes.

Many reporters came to Dayton to report on the trial. One of them was H. L. Mencken, a well-known critic and essayist. He wrote for the *Baltimore Sun*. Mencken's articles were clever. They influenced a lot of people. Mencken supported Scopes all through the trial.

Scopes was found guilty and fined $100. (H. L. Mencken paid his fine.) Scopes's conviction was later overturned by the state supreme court. In 1968, the U.S. Supreme Court said that a similar law was not constitutional.

Write an article reporting on the Scopes monkey trial, as Mencken might have written it for the *Baltimore Sun*.

1930's–1940's: The Depression and the New Deal

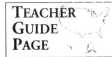

Skills: Research, organization, visual skills.

Objectives: Students understand the chronology of the Depression and the New Deal.

Project: Time line.

Suggested Group Roles: Reader, recorder, artist.

Suggested Group Size: Two to four students in each group.

Materials Needed: *The Depression and the New Deal* handout; blank paper, markers, colored pencils; research materials to be provided by students.

Procedure: Distribute handout and discuss with students. Form groups. If your U.S. history text provides good coverage of the period, you may direct students to read the relevant material in the text. Otherwise, set date for students to complete research and begin group work in class as directed in the handout. Display the completed time lines in the classroom.

Evaluation: Did students include at least 15 entries on their time lines? Did students use an appropriate scale for their time lines? Is the time line neatly and carefully executed? Did students include a title?

Variations:

1. Have students create a chart that shows the programs of the New Deal and what each program was designed to achieve.

2. Have students role-play a family trying to decide whether or not to leave their farm in Oklahoma during the 1930's.

1930's: The Depression and the New Deal

The 1920's were years of prosperity in America. Then suddenly, everything changed. The economy collapsed. Unemployment shot up. Banks were forced to close.

For farmers on the Great Plains, the Depression was made worse by drought. There was so little rain, crops dried up. Without the roots of plants to hold it together, the soil turned to dust. Winds sweeping across the Plains blew the topsoil away. The formerly fertile Great Plains now looked more like a desert. The area came to be called the "Dust Bowl." Many people had to give up their farms and look for work as migrant laborers.

President Hoover didn't seem able to cope with the Depression. When Franklin Roosevelt became president, he knew he had to do more than just improve the economy. He had to improve the spirits of the American people.

To do this, he started many different projects. Some of them gave direct relief to people who needed it. Some created jobs for people. Some encouraged actors, musicians, writers, and visual artists to create works for public enjoyment. Roosevelt started so many projects, with so many abbreviations, that his programs were called "alphabet soup." Roosevelt called it "a New Deal."

Find out about the Depression and the programs of the New Deal. Develop a time line to show some of the major events of the period from 1929 to 1945.

A time line should include at least 15 important entries. Choose a scale that relates to the entries chosen. Spread your entries out across the entire time line. Avoid having 8 or 10 entries within a few years of each other, with the remaining entries spread out over decades. Make sure the spaces between entries are in proper proportion—a 10-year gap should be much wider than a 1-year gap. If you wish, include illustrations for some of your entries. Give your finished time line a descriptive title.

1937: Missing—Amelia Earhart

Skills: Research, thinking, writing.

Objectives: Students explore how historians draw conclusions and develop a theory based on known facts and reasonable assumptions.

Project: Written first-person account.

Suggested Group Roles: Reader, recorder, checker.

Suggested Group Size: Two to three students in each group.

Materials Needed: *Missing—Amelia Earhart* handout; notebook paper and pens; research materials to be provided by students.

Procedure: Distribute handout and discuss with students. Form groups. Set date for students to complete research and begin group work in class as directed in the handout. After work is completed, discuss how incomplete much of our knowledge of history is. Historians often form reasonable theories based on a few known facts, then see if new information fits with the theory—as in the case of Amelia Earhart's disappearance.

Evaluation: Grade on completeness, accuracy, and originality.

1937: Missing—Amelia Earhart

In 1932, Amelia Earhart made international headlines. She became the first woman to fly alone across the Atlantic. Her flight from Newfoundland to Ireland, a distance of 2026 miles, took $13\frac{1}{2}$ hours to complete.

In 1937, Earhart was in the news again. On a flight across the Pacific Ocean, she disappeared.

People developed a lot of theories about what happened to her. Still, even today, nobody is sure of what really took place.

Find out as much as you can about Amelia Earhart's last flight. Read the different theories about her disappearance. Find out about the most recent investigations into her fate. Then choose the theory that you think is most likely.

Prepare a written account, according to your favorite theory, of this last flight. Write it in the first person, as if Amelia Earhart herself had written it.

Here are some questions you might ask to get started:

• Where did Amelia Earhart's last flight begin? _____

• Where did she plan to have the flight end? _____

• How far had she flown when she disappeared? _____

• Who was with her in the plane? _____

• Where was the plane last heard from? _____

• How do you explain her disappearance? _____

_____

1942: On the Home Front

Skills: Research, thinking, writing.

Objectives: Students learn about the effects of World War II on the American home front.

Project: Rationing chart.

Suggested Group Roles: Reader, recorder, coordinator.

Suggested Group Size: Three to five students in each group.

Materials Needed: *On the Home Front* handout; notebook paper and pens; research materials to be provided by students; blank paper and markers.

Procedure: Distribute handout and discuss with students. Form groups. Set date for students to complete research and begin group work in class as directed in the handout. Display completed charts in the classroom.

Teacher Background: About 20 essential items were rationed during the war, including sugar, coffee, fuel oil, gasoline, butter, meats, cheese, tires, rubber, metal, and even shoes. Other materials were not actually rationed but were in short supply. Salvage drives were held to collect tin cans, newspapers, rubber, waste fat, nylon and silk stockings, iron, and steel. Waste fat was processed to produce glycerin, needed in manufacturing bullets. Nylon and silk stockings were made into parachutes. When rubber supplies fell short, a synthetic rubber was developed.

Evaluation: Grade on completeness and accuracy.

Variations:

1. The rationing system was set up by the Office of Price Administration, or OPA. Have students role-play members of the OPA deciding how to allocate resources. For example, who should have priority on supplies of gasoline—doctors, or soldiers trying to see their families on leave?

(continued)

1942: On the Home Front *(continued)*

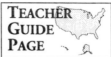

2. Rationed items became unavailable for a variety of reasons. Some were no longer imported because the ships that ordinarily carried them were being used to carry troops. Some—like rubber—were unavailable because primary sources for them were in Japan or countries in Southeast Asia conquered by Japan. Many metals were unavailable because they were now needed for tanks and armaments. Alcohol was used to make explosives. Assign one or two rationed items to each group. Have students investigate the reasons each item was rationed.

3. During the years between Pearl Harbor and V-J Day, the theme of war was everywhere in the United States. People listened to war poetry and watched war movies. Popular songs promoted salvage drives, war bonds, victory gardens, and all-around patriotism, with titles like "Get Out and Dig, Dig, Dig (Your Victory Garden)," "Junk Ain't Junk No More (Save and Salvage)," "Get Aboard the Bond Wagon," and "Remember Pearl Harbor." Have students compose lyrics for a song encouraging people to use as little as they could of rationed goods, so that more would be available for the war effort. If students wish, they can set their lyrics to the music of an existing song.

1942: On the Home Front

Most civilians in America didn't see World War II firsthand. The bombing of the fleet at Pearl Harbor in 1941 was the closest the combat of World War II came to the United States geographically. Still, almost everyone was affected by the war in some way.

Many things that had been available before the war were in short supply during the war years. Posters urged Americans to "Use it up, wear it out, make it do, or do without." Items in short supply went first to the war effort and soldiers serving abroad. Only then were they made available for the general population.

Some goods and products were rationed. This meant that the amount of an item you could buy was limited. Under the rationing system, everyone was given coupons for a certain share of rationed supplies. Once you had received your share, you could not get more of whatever it was.

Faced with shortages of everyday things, Americans improvised. They found—or invented—substitutes for some of the products they couldn't get during the war.

Prepare a list of things that were rationed in the United States during World War II. Then find out as much as you can about substitutes for these rationed goods. Make up a chart of the rationed items and their substitutes. When was each item first rationed? When did rationing end? Did any of the substitutes stay popular even after the rationed item became available again?

1950's: History from Things

Skills: Problem solving, writing, visual skills.

Objectives: Students consider the economic and social changes following World War II by seeing how historians can deduce information from artifacts.

Project: Written, illustrated report.

Suggested Group Roles: Recorder, artist, checker.

Suggested Group Size: Two to three students in each group.

Materials Needed: *History from Things* handout; notebook paper and pens; blank paper, markers, colored pencils. Optional: items made in the 1950's, or reproductions of such items; 1950's magazines.

Procedure: Distribute handout and discuss with students. If you wish, you might bring some typical 1950's items to show students or hand out magazines from the 1950's for students to examine. Form groups. Set date for students to complete research and begin group work in class as directed in the handout. Display completed reports in the classroom. After work is completed, discuss the way historians use artifacts to create a picture of a civilization or an era.

Evaluation: Grade on completeness, creativity, and artistic effectiveness of illustration.

1950's: History from Things

In the United States today, we are surrounded by things. Advertisers urge us to buy more things. They tell us that buying them will make us happier, or cleaner, or richer, or safer, or more attractive.

To most of us, things are just possessions. But to historians, things are artifacts. They can tell a story. A lot of the things we know today about the past come from a study of artifacts.

Your group is a team of archeologists in 2995. On an archeological dig, you have found a site dating to the 1950's in the United States. You have found an interesting artifact, one that tells you a lot about society in the 1950's.

Choose one common object in use during the 1950's. This will be your artifact. Imagine that you know nothing about the object or its use. What can you figure out about the artifact by examining it? What can it tell you about the society that made it?

Here are some questions you may want to ask:

- Was it an artistic creation, or was it meant to be used?

- If it was utilitarian (meant to be used), what was its function?

- What material is it made of?

- Is the material a natural substance or an artificial one?

- What does the purpose of the artifact tell you about the culture that used it?

- What can you learn about this culture's technology from the artifact?

- What can you learn about this culture's artistic tradition from the artifact?

- What might the artifact have meant for the person who made it? the person who used it?

Write a two-page report of your findings on this artifact. Illustrate your report with a drawing or photograph of the object you have studied.

1950's–1960's: Teenagers and the Civil Rights Movement

Skills: Research, thinking, writing, speaking.

Objectives: Students learn about the struggle for racial equality during the 1950's and 1960's.

Project: Speech, written and then delivered.

Suggested Group Roles: Reader, recorder, checker, speaker.

Suggested Group Size: Three to four students in each group.

Materials Needed: *Teenagers and the Civil Rights Movement* handout; notebook paper and pens; research materials to be provided by students.

Procedure: Distribute handout and discuss with students. Form groups. Set date for students to complete research and begin group work in class as directed in the handout. One student delivers the group's speech aloud to the class.

Teacher Background: Minniejean Brown, Eckford, Green, Mothershed, Pattillo, Ray, Roberts, Thomas, and Walls were "The Little Rock Nine," the nine high school students who integrated Little Rock High School. Collins, McNair, Robertson, and Wesley were the four girls killed in the Sixteenth Street Church bombing. Nine months before Rosa Parks and the Montgomery bus boycott, 15-year-old Claudette Colvin was arrested for refusing to move to the back of the bus when white passengers got on. Pat and Ricky Shuttlesworth tried to integrate a Birmingham high school in 1957; at the school, their father was beaten and their mother stabbed by a mob. Spottswood Bolling was one of the plaintiffs in a 1950 Washington, DC, case brought to integrate schools. Linda Brown was the Topeka, Kansas, 11-year-old whose case was one of the five decided by the Supreme Court in 1954 as *Brown* v. *Board of Education of Topeka, Kansas.*

Evaluation: Grade on written notes and oral presentation.

Variation: Assign a specific individual or group to each team. Remember that some individuals may be harder to find material on than others.

Special Tip: An excellent resource for this activity is *Freedom's Children: Young Civil Rights Activists Tell Their Own Stories,* by Ellen Levine (1993, G. P. Putnam's Sons, New York).

1950's and 1960's: Teenagers and the Civil Rights Movement

The Fourteenth Amendment to the Constitution became law in 1866. It promised African Americans the same rights as other American citizens.

This promise hasn't been kept. In the years after the Civil War, laws were passed that kept black Americans from voting in many areas. African Americans were kept from going to school with other Americans.

For years, African Americans in all walks of life fought for equal rights. In the 1950's and 1960's, their efforts—and the efforts of whites who supported them—started to bear fruit. A number of laws were passed to ensure that all citizens were treated equally.

Many people were active in the civil rights movement. Some names are very familiar—Rosa Parks and Martin Luther King, Jr., for example. But many young people were also involved.

Find out as much as you can about the young African Americans listed below. Then choose an individual or a group to discuss. Write a speech about this person or group, explaining how they contributed to the civil rights movement and thanking them for their contribution.

- Spottswood Bolling
- Linda Brown
- Minniejean Brown
- Addie Mae Collins
- Claudette Colvin
- Elizabeth Eckford
- Ernest Green
- Denise McNair
- Thelma Mothershed

- Melba Pattillo
- Gloria Ray
- Terrence Roberts
- Carole Robertson
- Pat Shuttlesworth
- Ricky Shuttlesworth
- Jefferson Thomas
- Carlotta Walls
- Cynthia Wesley

Have one group member deliver the speech aloud to the class.

1960's: El Teatro Campesino

Skills: Research, writing, speaking, visual skills.

Objectives: Students explore contemporary culture as it affects Hispanic Americans.

Project: One-act play, written and then staged.

Suggested Group Roles: Reader, recorder, coordinator.

Suggested Group Size: Four to five students in each group.

Materials Needed: *El Teatro Campesino* handout; notebook paper and pens; blank paper, markers, colored pencils; research materials to be provided by students; props and other dramatic materials to be provided by students.

Procedure: Distribute handout and discuss with students. Form groups. Set date for students to complete research and begin group work in class as directed in the handout. Students present their actos for the class.

Teacher Background: For more information about actos and El Teatro Campesino, see the article "El Acto: Studying the Hispanic American Experience Through the Farm Worker Theater," by George W. Chilcoat, in the July/August 1995 issue of *The Social Studies.*

Evaluation: Did students grasp the central concepts of the activity? Did the acto present an issue relevant to Hispanic American history or culture?

Variation: An extension of the acto was known as the super-acto. This was a combination of several actos about one event. To present a super-acto, direct each group to prepare an acto based on a different incident in one event—for example, the 1965 Delano grape boycott that began La Huelga. Then have the groups present their actos in the order in which they would have actually taken place chronologically.

1960's: El Teatro Campesino

Migrant farmworkers have often been taken advantage of. Moving from place to place, they find it hard to get an education. Employers sometimes pay poor wages for long hours. Since the migrant workers don't stay in one place for very long, it's hard for them to organize and demand better treatment.

During the 1960's, an activist named César Chavez began a union for migrant farmworkers. The union called for strikes against California grape growers who treated migrants unfairly. The public was urged to boycott—stay away from, not buy—certain varieties of grapes. This movement was called La Huelga, or The Strike.

One of the problems for organizers of La Huelga was letting migrant workers know what was happening. A farmworkers' theater, El Teatro Campesino, was formed to do this. The Teatro developed a play form known as *el acto*. The acto was a short play, just one act long. Actos focused on Chicano themes. Subjects ranged from migrant workers to Latino history and culture and the struggles of the Hispanic community.

Only a few characters appeared in an acto. They were identified by masks or signs hung around their necks. This way the audience didn't have to try to figure out who people were meant to be. The actors used exaggerated body movements to help show the action. Dialogue was usually simple. Signs and placards were sometimes used to explain events.

Each acto had five goals. It tried to make a specific point about a social problem. It tried to show what people thought about the problem. It tried to show what the opposition was doing. It tried to suggest a solution. And it aimed to inspire the audience to get involved in social action.

Keeping these guidelines in mind, prepare an acto of your own. Choose an event involving Hispanic Americans. You can choose a current event, or one in the past. Research this event and decide what makes it important. Then develop an acto to illustrate it. If you wish, you can design simple scenery to go with your acto. Remember to include masks or signs to identify your characters. Then stage—act out—your acto for the class.

1990's: All the News That's Fit to Print

Skills: Problem solving, writing, visual skills.

Objectives: Students understand that the same event can be presented in different ways by the media.

Project: Comparative chart.

Suggested Group Roles: Recorder, coordinator.

Suggested Group Size: Three to four students in each group.

Materials Needed: *All the News* . . . handout; notebook paper and pens; blank paper, markers, colored pencils; current newspapers accessed by students.

Procedure: Distribute handout and discuss with students. Form groups. Set date for students to complete research and begin group work in class as directed in the handout. Display completed charts in the classroom. After work is completed, discuss the fact that media coverage of an event is always selective and must be evaluated by the reader, viewer, or listener.

Evaluation: Did a group choose four events to track? Did the group check coverage provided by both print and broadcast media? Did group members combine their findings in a chart? Is the chart neatly executed?

Name _____ Date _____

 1990's: All the News That's Fit to Print

Pick four events you see reported in today's newspaper. Try to include one local, one regional, one state, and one national event. For one week, see how each event is covered by the media. Different group members can watch different TV news programs, read different newspapers, listen to different radio news reports. Compare the different ways the subject is covered. Does the way a subject is covered change as time passes? Which news source do you think provided the most complete and objective coverage? Create a chart that shows your findings.

You can use a form like the one below to organize your notes.

Event 1: _____

TV news: _____

Newspapers: _____

Radio news: _____

Event 2: _____

TV news: _____

Newspapers: _____

Radio news: _____

Event 3: _____

TV news: _____

Newspapers: _____

Radio news: _____

Event 4: _____

TV news: _____

Newspapers: _____

Radio news: _____

1600's–1990's: Historical Party

Skills: Research, problem solving, writing, speaking.

Objectives: Students identify and describe important individuals from different historical periods.

Project: Written party plan and guest list.

Suggested Group Roles: Reader, recorder, coordinator, speaker.

Suggested Group Size: Three to four students in each group.

Materials Needed: *Historical Party* handout; notebook paper and pens.

Procedure: Distribute handout and discuss with students. Form groups and have students work as directed in the handout. Groups read their lists to the class and describe their planned party.

Evaluation: Did groups include at least 10 names? Did groups give a reason for each invitation? Did groups make notes describing other party arrangements? Did groups do a good job in presenting this to the class orally?

Variations:

1. Assign one historical period to each group. Combine the party plans for an overview of the students' choices for the most important people throughout U.S. history.

2. Assign a different set of guests to each group. One should choose scientists, one writers, one artists, one actors, one politicians, etc. Then the whole class should choose a final combined guest list from the small-group lists.

Name _____ Date _____

 1600's–1990's: Historical Party

You love to give parties, and everyone always enjoys the ones you organize. You always take care of all the details so your guests have a good time.

One of your favorite parts of setting up a party is planning the guest list. Some people just invite one crowd to a party, but you like to mix different groups. Your idea of the perfect party is one where politicians mix with poets, and painters talk to plumbers. You enjoy writers, scientists, musicians, mechanics—anyone with something to say.

You've been given an unbelievable opportunity by a local inventor. She's developed a time machine. You can bring up to 20 people from any periods in history forward for a party. The only limitation is that at the time each person is picked up, he or she must be in North America.

Make up a plan for your party. Write down the names of your guests and the reason you have invited each one. You must invite at least 10 people, but you can invite as many as 20.

Make notes about the other party arrangements.

Here are some questions you might ask to get you started:

• Whom will you invite?

• What are your criteria for choosing your guests?

• How do you think the party will go?

• Will people get along well, or have you chosen people who are likely to get into arguments?

• What foods will you serve?

• What entertainment will you provide?

When you are done, read your guest list to the class and describe your planned party.

1783–1990's: Broken Treaties

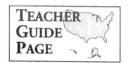
Skills: Research, thinking, map skills.

Objectives: Students examine the political and territorial dealings between European Americans and Native Americans from the early years of European settlement until today.

Project: Historical maps.

Suggested Group Roles: Reader, recorder, artist.

Suggested Group Size: Two to three students in each group.

Materials Needed: *Broken Treaties* handout; notebook paper and pens; blank paper, markers, colored pencils; research material to be provided by students. Optional: blank outline map of the United States on page 131.

Procedure: Distribute handout and discuss with students. If you wish, give students copies of the blank outline map of the United States. Form groups. Set date for students to complete research and begin group work in class as directed in the handout. Display completed maps in class.

Teacher Background: In 1783, Indians held everything but the areas that are now the states of Maine, New Hampshire, Vermont, Massachusetts, Rhode Island, Connecticut, New York, New Jersey, Pennsylvania, Delaware, Maryland, Virginia, North Carolina, South Carolina, Florida, and West Virginia. Parts of Georgia, Alabama, Mississippi, Louisiana, and Texas were under European control, but most of these areas were still held by Native Americans.

By 1810, Europeans had taken control of parts of Michigan, Ohio, Indiana, Illinois, Kentucky, Tennessee, Oklahoma, Arkansas, Kansas, Nebraska, Iowa, and Missouri, as well as more of Georgia and Mississippi.

By 1850, Indian control had been pushed back to include very little land east of 95°W longitude, with the states of Wisconsin, Illinois, Iowa, Missouri, Arkansas, and Louisiana being entirely under European control, as well as most of Oklahoma, Kansas, and Nebraska.

(continued)

1783–1990's: Broken Treaties
(continued)

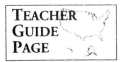
By 1870, Native American lands had been reduced to areas in the states of Washington, Idaho, Montana, the Dakotas, Minnesota, Wyoming, Colorado, Nevada, Arizona, Utah, New Mexico, and Texas.

Today, Native Americans hold only isolated pockets of land, mostly in western states. Most of these areas are not the ancestral lands of the peoples who now live there.

Evaluation: Did students create at least three maps? Do maps clearly show the progressive change in the ownership of the land?

Variation: Assign one date to each group to create a map showing Indian possessions. Possible dates include:

1680—after King Philip's War

1700—early British settlements

1713—after French Wars

1760—after French and Indian Wars, before Revolution

1784—after Revolution

1810

1850

1870

Today

1783–1990's: Broken Treaties

The history of contact between Europeans and Native Americans is a history of broken promises, of treaties set aside whenever it became convenient. When the first Europeans arrived, Indians lived in every part of the land.

In 1783, when U.S. independence was officially established, Native Americans had been pushed from the eastern seaboard, but they still held most of the land in the continent.

Today, 200 years later, Indian control is limited to small pockets of land, often land not wanted by whites.

Find out as much as you can about the history of how the land passed from Native American control to European-American hands. Then create a series of maps to show this history, from 1783 to today.

You should create at least three maps, but you can create more if you want. Be sure to include a key and a caption for each map.

1600's–1990's: Public Schools

Skills: Thinking, writing.

Objectives: Students explore how cultural institutions change over time.

Project: Comparative chart.

Suggested Group Roles: Recorder, coordinator.

Suggested Group Size: Two to three students in each group.

Materials Needed: *Public Schools* handout; notebook paper and pens.

Procedure: Distribute handout and discuss with students. Form groups and have students work as directed in the handout. Display completed charts in class. After work is completed, use the results to discuss the way institutions we are familiar with today have evolved since they were first set up.

Evaluation: Grade on accuracy, completeness, and neatness.

1600's–1990's: Public Schools

Education in America has a long history. In 1647, Massachusetts passed a law saying towns with 50 or more families had to set up schools. In 1852, Massachusetts was the first state to say that it wasn't enough just to make schools available. Students had to attend school for a certain number of days every year.

Schools in the early days were very unlike schools today. The school was usually a one-room building, where all students were taught together by one teacher. The building was usually heated by a wood stove at one end. Parents were expected to provide firewood for the school. They also paid a small tuition fee.

In many areas, school was only held for a few months in the winter. That was the only time when children were not needed to work on their families' farms. Students came from a large area to the school. They came on foot or by horseback, often traveling several miles each way.

The three R's back then were reading, writing, and religion. Arithmetic was not added to the curriculum until the late 1600's. Children learned to read using a hornbook. This was a sheet of paper attached to a board and protected by a thin, transparent layer of horn. To write, students used a slate and slate pencil.

Teachers were often only slightly more educated than their students. They usually didn't have any formal training in teaching. The usual teaching method was constant drilling. Discipline was often harsh.

Some teachers moved on a regular rotation from place to place. Few stayed long in one location.

Schools in America have changed in many ways since those days. Prepare a chart to compare education then and now. On one side of the chart, list some of the features of education described above. On the other side, describe that feature of education today. Give your chart a title, and create headings for both lists.

1903–1990's: Evolution of the Airplane

Skills: Research, visual skills.

Objectives: Students see how technology and society affect each other.

Project: Historical poster.

Suggested Group Roles: Reader, recorder, artist.

Suggested Group Size: Three to four students in each group.

Materials Needed: *Evolution of the Airplane* handout; research materials to be provided by students; notebook paper and pens; large blank paper or poster board; markers, colored pencils.

Procedure: Distribute handout and discuss with students. Form groups. Set date for students to complete research and begin group work in class as directed in the handout. Display completed posters in the classroom.

Evaluation: Grade on completeness, accuracy, neatness, and attractiveness of design.

1903–1990's: Evolution of the Airplane

On December 8, 1903, an article in *The New York Times* stated that humans would not fly for 1000 years. Nine days later, Orville and Wilbur Wright proved the newspaper to be wrong. Their wood and canvas biplane, powered by a 12-horsepower engine, remained airborne for 59 seconds and traveled a distance of 852 feet.

The airplane has changed a lot since then. By the 1920's, airplanes were no longer a mere framework, open to the elements. Both cabin and cockpit were closed in.

In the 1930's, the pressurized aircraft cabin was introduced. This allowed planes to cruise as high as 20,000 feet, above much of the bad weather that made flying so uncomfortable

During the 1940's, the jet engine was developed.

In the 1970's, jets that could fly faster than the speed of sound were introduced. Today's airplanes routinely fly at speeds of 600 miles an hour.

Find out as much as you can about the history of the airplane. Then prepare a poster to show the history of air transportation. Use photocopies and original drawings to show the major aircraft developments since the Kitty Hawk Flyer of 1903. Be sure to label each illustration, and describe why it represented an important development.

1600's–1990's: How Old Is America?

Skills: Problem solving, visual skills.

Objectives: Students learn to see the history of the United States in a broader historical context.

Project: Historical graphic.

Suggested Group Roles: Recorder, artist.

Suggested Group Size: Two to three students in each group.

Materials Needed: *How Old Is America?* handout; blank paper, markers, colored pencils.

Procedure: Distribute handout and discuss with students. Form groups and have students work as directed in the handout. Display completed graphics in class.

Teacher Background: Here's one effective way to show these data. Each country is represented by a stack of "tiles." Each tile represents a certain number of years; 100 years is a convenient measure. At the top of each stack, show a map of the country being represented. Thus the stack representing Egypt would be 50 tiles high, while the U.S. stack would be only 3.77 units high, with the others falling in between.

Evaluation: Does the graphic show the data clearly? Are all the data included?

1600's–1990's: How Old Is America?

When we study U.S. history, there is a lot to learn. It sometimes seems that the United States has existed for a long time. But if we compare our history with the history of other parts of the world, it's actually very short.

Organized government in the United States probably began in 1619. This is when the House of Burgesses in Jamestown, Virginia, was set up. Using 1619 as a starting date, we can say that in 1996, this country has had an organized government for 377 years.

Here are some figures showing the history of organized government in other parts of the world:

Egypt	5,000 years
Greece	3,600 years
China	3,000 years
France	1,000 years
United Kingdom	900 years
Russia	500 years
Spain	500 years

Choose a graphic way to present these figures. You could use a graph, a chart, a time line, or any other graphic approach. Your graphic should clearly show how short the history of government is in this country, compared with other parts of the world.

Name _____ Date _____

Outline Map of the United States